NUTRiBULLET®
Life Changing Recipes

Table of contents

15-piece set includes:

1 High-torque Power Base

New! Flip-Top To-Go Lid
with Oversized Cup

1 Short Cup

2 Extractor Blades

2 Tall Cups with 1 Handled Lip Ring
and one Regular Lip Ring

2 Stay-fresh Resealable Lids

Bonus Life Changing Recipes Book

1 Pocket Nutritionist

1 Pocket Nutritionist

- MAX -

Add water to **MAX** line

Add "boost"

50% fruit

50% leafy greens
(2 cups = 1 serving)

NutriBlast

What is a nutriblast?

The NutriBlast is a nutrient extracted drink designed to feed your system as many servings of easily absorbable fruits and vegetables as possible. All variations follow a very simple basic formula: **50% leafy greens, 50% fruit, and ¼ cup of seeds, nuts, or "super boosts." Add enough water to cover ingredients, twist on the blade, and blend.**

The NutriBlast makes an ideal breakfast beverage, but you can enjoy extracted nutrition any time of the day! You will be amazed by how energetic and healthy you feel from enjoying this satisfying raw **NUTRITION-EXTRACTED** goodness every day!

Start with one NutriBlast a day. As you begin to feel the amazing rewards that accompany a diet rich in **NUTRITION-EXTRACTED** foods, feel free to enjoy TWO NutriBlasts a day. Boundless energy, restful sleep, mental clarity, and the overall feeling of well being that comes from true nourishment await! The more you blast, the better you'll feel!

Extraction Instructions:

Twist the Extractor Blade onto the Tall Cup and tighten by hand to make sure the vessel is sealed.
Press the vessel blade side-down onto the Power Base and extract for no longer than 1 minute. If more extraction is needed, wait 1 minute, then repeat the extraction process in 1 minute intervals up to 3 times as needed to achieve the desired consistency. If more than 3 1-minute extractions are needed, allow the power base to cool for 2-3 minutes after the third extraction before beginning the next round.

CAUTION: DO NOT RUN THE POWER BASE IN EXCESS OF 1 MINUTE PER INTERVAL. DO NOT RUN THE POWER BASE FOR MORE THAN 3 1-MINUTE INTERVALS WITHOUT ALLOWING IT TO COOL FOR 2-3 MINUTES AFTER THE THIRD EXTRACTION. RUNNING THE MOTOR FOR MORE THAN 1 MINUTE CONSECUTIVELY IN ANY INTERVAL MAY RESULT IN PERMANENT DAMAGE TO THE POWER BASE.

NOTE: The information contained in our guide and recipe book is not a substitute for regular health care. Always consult your physician regarding health and nutrition.

How it works

Extracting

1 Fill ingredients into the **Tall Cup**.

2 Twist the **Extractor Blade** onto the **Tall Cup** and tighten by hand to make sure the vessel is sealed.

3 Press the vessel blade side-down onto the **Power Base** and extract for no longer than 1 minute. If more extraction is needed, wait 1 minute, then repeat the extraction process in 1 minute intervals up to 3 times as needed to achieve the desired consistency. If more than 3 1-minute extractions are needed, allow the power base to cool for 2-3 minutes after the third extraction before beginning the next round.

CAUTION: Do not run the Power Base in excess of 1 minute per interval. Do not run the power base for more than 3 1-minute intervals without allowing it to cool for 2-3 minutes after the third extraction. Running the motor for more than 1 minute consecutively in any interval may result in permanent damage to the Power Base.

Shake Technique

If the cup's contents are not blending evenly, use this technique to ensure all ingredients reach the blade:

1. Remove the cup and blade assembly from the Power Base.

2. Shake the cup and blade assembly like a cocktail shaker to move solid ingredients toward the blade. Return the cup and blade assembly to the Power Base and resume blending. Repeat if necessary.

Tap Technique

Use this technique if ingredients are clinging to the sides of the cup.

1. Remove the cup and blade assembly from the Power Base.

2. Tap the blade side of the cup/blade assembly on the counter with enough force to dislodge ingredients from the sides of the cup. Be careful not to tap too hard to avoid damaging the unit.

3. Return the cup and blade assembly to the Power Base and resume blending. Repeat if necessary.

Are you getting the most out of your food?

Food is the fuel that powers our lives, the source of nutrients that gives our body energy to carry out its internal and external functions. At least, that's what food *should* be.

Unfortunately, in this day and age, many of us eat far too many packaged, processed foods that fail to give us the life-sustaining nutrients we need. But even those that eat healthfully still have problems processing the nutrients needed to stay vibrant and energized. While basing our diets on real, unprocessed vegetables, fruits, whole grains, seeds, nuts, and legumes is important for overall health and wellness, it may not be enough to maximize the nutritional potential these foods can offer.

To reach optimum health and take advantage of the disease-fighting compounds within our food, we must not only eat healthfully, but also fully *absorb* the nutrients our food contains. This is where the NutriBullet 900 Series comes in. This powerful machine extracts healthful plant foods into liquid form, breaking them down so your body doesn't have to.

When you drink NutriBlasts—the powerful drinks made in the NutriBullet—you are delivering food to your body in its *most absorbable state*, sparing your digestive system the work of breaking food down to unlock the nutrition within. Without straining to dissolve large pieces of food, your digestive system can absorb all of the goodness your food has to offer.

So what are you waiting for? Grab yourself some fruits and veggies and start extracting; you'll be amazed at what the NutriBullet can do for you!

So how do we
reclaim our health?

To avoid the horrible health consequences associated with the consumption of processed, packaged "food," the answer is simple: don't eat it. Instead, feed your body fruits, vegetables, whole grains, nuts, seeds, legumes, and small amounts of Hormone-free meat prepared as close to their natural state as possible.

While this advice addresses **what** we feed our bodies, we must also examine **how** we consume the food we choose. Even those who eat the healthiest diets may not be absorbing the maximum amount of nutrients their food has to offer. This is especially true for people over 50, as the digestive system becomes less efficient with age.

Additionally, many of us do not take the time to properly chew our food—especially with high-fiber whole foods like fruits, vegetables, seeds, and nuts. This leaves the brunt of food breakdown to the stomach and its digestive enzymes, which, though powerful, may struggle to dissolve large pieces of food. As a result, the intestines become loaded, clogged, and unable to extract the full nutrient potential of your food.

This is where the NutriBullet comes into play. The NutriBullet helps your body absorb nutrients by essentially pre-digesting your food for you. And unlike juicers that eliminate beneficial fiber from your produce and blenders that leave large chunks of food for your stomach to dissolve, the NutriBullet breaks fruits, vegetables, nuts, and seeds down into their most absorbable state while retaining all of the nutrition they have to offer.

Incorporating NutriBullet-extracted drinks—also known as NutriBlasts—into your daily routine is an excellent way to ensure your body receives the nutrition it needs and deserves!

Here is the basic formula for the delicious, refreshing, and highly absorbable NutriBlast:

- 50% greens

- 50% fruit and/or vegetables

- 2 Tbsp combined "boosts" (nuts, seeds, or super food*)

- water, unsweetened tea, coconut water, or unsweetened almond milk to the **MAX LINE**

*Super Foods detailed in the following section

Everyday Food vs. SUPERFOOD

While all plant foods offer a multitude of nutritional benefits, there are a handful of crops that contain exceptionally dense nutrient concentrations. These foods are known as Super Foods and grow in specific regions all over the world.

Adding just a small amount of Superfoods to your NutriBlast can take it from a healthy beverage to a nutritional powerhouse—giving your body high quality vitamins and minerals that can not only fuel your daily activity, but also potentially repair cell damage and increase energy, stamina, and longevity.

The NutriBullet has searched far and wide to bring you four of the world's greatest superfoods: Cacao Nibs, Chia Seeds, Goji Berries, and Maca Root Powder.

These four plant foods not only supply amazing nourishment, but also represent longstanding traditions of cultivation, harvest, and cultural significance in their native lands.

At the NutriBullet, we have painstakingly researched the sources of these superfoods to bring to you the freshest, most sustainably farmed organic crops available. We are proud to offer raw, certified organic superfoods sourced from ecologically and community-conscious farms throughout the world.

We believe that eating well can truly make the world a healthier place. When you include our boosts in your daily NutriBlast, you not only feed yourself superior nutrition to fuel your unique purpose; you also support the individuals and communities that give their life's energy to feed you. And that's a cycle we can all endorse.

SOME FOODS MAY INTERACT WITH MEDICATIONS OR CAUSE SIDE EFFECTS IN THOSE WITH CERTAIN MEDICAL CONDITIONS. CHECK WITH YOUR DOCTOR BEFORE CHANGING YOUR DIET, ESPECIALLY IF YOU ARE PREGNANT, NURSING, OR TAKING MEDICATION FOR AN EXISTING MEDICAL CONDITION.

Raw Organic
cacao nibs

You've probably heard it before, but sometimes news this good bears repeating: Chocolate is good for you!

And not just good for you—raw, unprocessed cacao is one of nature's best sources of nutrition. Loaded with magnesium, antioxidants, and brain-stimulating chemicals, cacao helps the body absorb calcium, fight disease, and stabilize moods.

History

Cacao's use as a health food dates back millennia to the ancient Olmec tribe that populated the tropical terrain of south-central Mexico from 1200 to 300 BCE. The Olmecs domesticated the cacao tree, paving its use for the Mayan, Toltec, and Aztec civilizations that came to populate the same area over the course of the next 1000 years.

All three civilizations bestowed spiritual powers onto cacao and incorporated it into their religious ceremonies and mythology. By the time the Aztecs introduced the crop to Spanish explorers in the 16th and 17th centuries, it had been transformed into currency and used as food only by the very wealthy, who mixed it into a dark, bitter drink with various spices. It was the Spanish explorers who brought the crop to Europe and mixed it with sugar and dairy to form the chocolate we know and love today.

Now, with the discovery of the vast nutritional benefits unprocessed cacao holds, many are seeking to enjoy the bean in its original unaltered form.

Quality Control

Our raw, organic cacao nibs are sourced using fair-trade practices from small cooperative farms in the South American countries of Peru and Ecuador. They are certified organic and placed under strict quality control measures. Temperatures are kept below 115 degrees Fahrenheit throughout the journey from farm to table, making our nibs truly raw to retain maximum nutritional value.

The cacao nibs found in these packages are chocolate in its purest form. Unpolluted with the sugar, dairy, and stabilizers that classify commercial chocolate as "junk food," cacao nibs provide bittersweet chocolate decadence and superior "super food" nutrition to any mixture! Extract them with berry, banana, or even avocado to give your NutriBlast the taste and feel of a sinful dessert. Mix them in homemade banana nut bread or granola bars to add depth and texture to nutritious treats, or grind them into powder with your Exctractor Blade and mix with heated almond milk for a superfood hot chocolate! The possibilities are endless!

Raw Organic
chia seeds

Until recently, any mention of the word "chia" was most likely led by "ch-ch-ch," but these tiny seeds pack a nutritional punch that far exceed their novelty gift appeal. Filled with more Omega-3 fatty acids than salmon, more calcium per fluid ounce than milk, and significant amounts of fiber, iron, calcium, magnesium, potassium, B-vitamins, and antioxidants, chia seeds make an incredible addition to any diet.

Chia seeds are also one of the most naturally balanced sources of healthy fats, containing the ideal ratio of Omega-3 to Omega-6 fatty acids. Their complex nutritional profile and high fiber content help the body stabilize blood sugar levels, a quality that makes them excellent mix-ins with high sugar and starchy fruits and vegetables. They are also mildly flavored and form a gelled coating when added to liquids, making them excellent natural thickening agents for NutriBlasts, vegan-baked goods, and nutritious puddings.

History

Native to Central America, chia (meaning "strength" in Mayan) has been celebrated for its health benefits for centuries. The seed was a staple crop of the region's many historical civilizations, including the Olmecs, the Mayans, and the Aztecs—all of whom noted its powerful energy-giving properties. The legendary Aztec messengers turned to the simple seed to fuel their hundred-mile treks through region's highlands. Today, the Central American superfood is making waves as a nutritional powerhouse all over the world. At the NutriBullet, we are proud to share our top-quality, raw, organic certified chia seeds with you!

Quality Control

Our raw, organic chia seeds are grown pesticide-free in Ecuador, where they are harvested at peak ripeness to ensure their highest nutritional value. Our chia is grown according to fair trade principals, and dried using solar power, so the seeds in this package are not only good for you, but good for the community and the environment as well!

Raw Organic
goji berries

Native to the Himalayan highlands of China and Tibet, the goji berry is one of nature's most nutritionally complete foods. These "red diamonds," as they are called in their homeland, contain 18 different amino acids—including 8 of the 9 essential food-based amino acids that our bodies cannot manufacture on their own.

Goji berries also contain up to 21 trace minerals, including zinc, iron, copper, calcium, germanium, selenium, and phosphorus. Goji berries are the richest source of carotenoids of all known foods or plants on earth, containing even more beta carotene per serving than carrots! Goji berries also contain 500 times the vitamin C content per weight of oranges, ranking them second only to camu camu berries as the planet's richest source of vitamin C. In addition to all of these amazing nutrients, goji berries also contain vitamins B1, B2, B6, and vitamin E.

History

Goji berries play a large role in the enduring practices of ancient Chinese medicine. The berries have been praised for their eye, liver, and kidney-supporting properties in ancient Chinese medical texts dating as far back as 5,000 years. It is widely believed in Chinese medicine that gojis increase the "chi," or life energy in those who eat them.

Legendary Chinese healers and medical texts praise the berry for its vitality-boosting benefits. In his early medical work (475-221 B.C.), famed healer Shen Nung Ben Tsao noted the berry's ability to replenish vital essences and strengthen and heal vital organs.

In more recent times, the legendary Master Li Qing Yuen, a Chinese herbalist who many claim to have lived to 252 years of age (1678-1930) known to consume goji berries daily whether exagerated or true, the life of Li Qing Yuen is one of the most well-documented cases of longevity in history. The goji berry's healthful reputation endures today, far beyond the borders of its native terrain.

Quality Control

The NUTRIBULLET is proud to offer you the incredible health benefits of raw, organic goji berries. Sourced from a pristine, USDA-certified organic region in the Ningxia province of China—the same region that holds the annual Goji Berry Festival—all of the goji berries we offer are harvested with exceptional care, sun-dried in accordance with raw temperature regulations and then carefully selected, twice inspected, and lab-tested for purity before packaging.

Raw Organic
maca powder

Praised for centuries for its adaptogenic (stress-regulating) properties, maca root, and the powder derived from it help the body control a wide array of energy-altering functions, from focus and attention to libido and fertility. The Incan civilization of the Andes mountains first cultivated Maca root for as long as 2,000 years ago. Prized for its superior nutritional value, the Incans considered maca to be a gift of the gods and used it as currency throughout the course of their history. Today, maca is gaining popularity as a true super food.

As one of the few plants to thrive in the rocky soil and high altitudes of the Andes mountains, maca not only contains the important vitamins and minerals found in most root vegetables, but also contains unique phytochemicals that neutralize acids in the body when ingested.

Maca is also unique in that it contains 8 of the 9 essential amino acids—protein-building compounds that the body must obtain from external food sources. Additionally, this powerful root contains fiber, vitamins E and C, calcium, potassium, and iron, as well as immune-boosting compounds known as glucosinolates.

With its libido-enhancing, energy-boosting, and immune building properties, maca is on the top of the list of foods that increase vitality. In fact, maca is so powerful, that it is recommended to introduce it to your diet in small amounts. We suggest you incorporate maca into your routine in four week-long stages:

Week 1: use 1 tsp of maca 3-4 days/week
Week 2: use 1 tsp of maca 5-6 days/week
Week 3: use 2 tsp of maca 5 days/week
Week 4: use 1 Tbsp of maca 4 days/week

Once you have built your tolerance to maca, continue to use 2 tsp to 1 Tbsp of the powder 4-5 times per week. You will no doubt notice a difference in your overall energy, wellness, and vitality.

Quality Control

Harvested in the 2 ½ mile-high altitudes of Peru, the Maca root used for the NutriBullet's raw, organic Maca powder is one of the few world crops unpolluted by the chemicals and industrial waste that accompany the overwhelming majority of modern farming techniques. The NutriBullet's Maca Powder is derived from a combination of black, yellow, and red maca roots harvested at peak ripeness; it is processed according to strict quality standards that preserve the delicate and powerfully nutritious phytochemicals within the roots.

We at the NutriBullet have worked hard to ensure that our maca powder comes from socially and environmentally conscious growers. By purchasing our maca, you support the fair pay and livelihood of Peruvian farmers and the preservation of their bountiful farmland for years to come.

Ordering
nutribullet superfoods

All of the organic, ethically sourced NutriBullet Superfoods mentioned are available for purchase at
www.NutriLiving.com or at **www.nutribullet.com/accessories**

SuperFood SuperBoost

Are you ready to supercharge your Nutriblasts?

Super boost your NutriBlasts with this unique combination of 4 top superfoods – cacao, chia, maca and goji! Made with premium quality, pure, organic, superfood ingredients from around the world. Just add a scoop of this easy-to-use formula to your daily NutriBlast for a BURST of extra nutrition. This formula is perfect for those looking to strengthen joints, detox, promote normal sleep habits, support the immune system, and increase vitality to look and feel better than you have in years.

Cacao Nibs

Boost your energy and your mood!

Chock full of more antioxidants than red wine or green tea, cacao is chocolate in its most natural form! Cacao is David Wolfe's #1 superfood because it tastes great AND is an amazing source of magnesium, which is vital for healthy heart function and which helps build strong bones, relax muscles, and create a feeling of calmness.

Cacao also contains over 300 compounds including protein, fat, carbohydrates, fiber, iron, zinc, copper, calcium and sulfur, which helps to regulate blood sugar and maintain healthy joints. This is chocolate the way nature intended... so go ahead and add cacao to your daily NutriBlast!

Organic Chia Seeds

Detox and slim down!

Chia is the ancient Mayan word for strength and these tiny seeds are full of nutrients that help keep your body strong. Packed with omega-3 fatty acids, rich in antioxidants, and known as one of the best sources of complete, plant-based protein, the nutritionally-dense chia seed blends easily into a variety of flavors.

When exposed to liquid, the fibrous coating on the outside of chia seeds swells up and turns into a gel. When consumed, this flavorless chia gel is great for drawing toxins out of the intestines, making you feel full and for keeping things moving in the digestive tract. Add these tiny seeds your daily NutriBlast to reap some big health rewards!

Organic Goji Berries

Reverse the signs of aging!

Goji Berries are the most nutritionally-dense fruits on Earth. They are loaded with vitamin C, contain 15 times more iron than spinach, and have the highest concentration of protein of any fruit!

This mighty little superfruit, known in Chinese medicine for increasing strength and longevity, also contains anti-inflammatory, antibacterial and anti-fungal compounds as well as calcium, zinc, selenium and many other important trace minerals.

Include these tiny nutritional powerhouses in your daily NutriBlast!

Organic Maca Powder

De-stress and re-energize!

Harvested above 12,000 feet in the Andes mountains, maca is one of the only edible plants that grows at such extreme altitudes. To survive in this harsh environment, the maca root developed unique adaptive properties, properties that benefit our bodies as well.

When ingested, maca root powder supports the body's natural stress response, boosts energy, improves performance, and promotes optimal hormone balance. With a malty, nutty flavor, this amazing superfood blends well into creamy NutriBlasts. Enjoy maca a few days per week.

Live the Nutri-Lifestyle on
NUTRiLiving.com

NutriLiving.com is a community for NutriBullet owners centered entirely around your personal health needs. Not everyone is the same, after all, and not everyone should get the same advice for healthy living. That's why we've gathered experts on nutrition – Registered Dietitians, Nutritionists, trained community moderators and more – to provide you with the information you can't find anywhere else, all in one place.

We're here to help you learn all you can about your health. From fibromyalgia recovery information to weight loss advice and more, the content featured on this site will help you grow healthier, happier, and more vibrant, all with your NUTRIBULLET in hand! We've got articles, recipes, video information on healing foods, and even a forum and profile page where you can interact with other Blasters and share your stories, experiences, questions and more. It's the support you need right at your fingertips. All you need to get started is your NutriBullet serial number.

Go to **Nutriliving.com** today and join the fun!

How
NUTRiLiving.com
can change your life

About Articles

We've got hundreds of informational articles written by our experts, nutritionists, and Registered Dietitians that not only describe the history, symptoms and effects of certain illnesses, but try to help you avoid them altogether.

They're indexed and entirely searchable. Feel free to search by topic or peruse the most recent additions.

About Healing Foods

NutriLiving.com features the Healing Foods section, a glossary of every fruit, vegetable, nut and seed you can possibly think of! This guide describes the health benefits, selection process, and interesting facts surrounding your favorite blast-able ingredients!

Search by fruit, ailment, vitamin or mineral and see what you find.

About Success Stories

Don't think Blasting will actually better your health? We've got incredible testimonials in our Success Stories section that would say otherwise! Give them a quick scan and get inspired!

About Recipes

NutriLiving also contains hundreds of never-before-seen recipes! Search an ingredient or ailment to find related recipes, or take your chances, click a random recipe, and get blasting!

About the Forum

Interact directly with other NutriBullet users to share experiences, stories, recipes, and more! Create a profile, upload your photo and bio, and write on fellow users' feeds. You'll be surprised at the amount of support you'll receive once you start posting.

About your News Feed

Consider your news feed your personal NutriLiving command center. Update your status, read how your friends are doing, and catch up on the latest content based on your own specific interests.

Cheers to your
health! *Blasting to prevent and relieve illness.*

In addition to improving overall health and wellness, the NutriBullet is an excellent tool for those suffering from a wide variety of health problems. This portion of this book focuses on some of the most common ailments facing the American public today, and shares information, recipes, and stories from NutriBullet users who have drastically improved their condition by incorporating NutiBlasts into their diets. Read their inspirational stories, peruse our recipes, and see firsthand how you can benefit from adopting the NutriBullet lifestyle.

Cancer Prevention & recovery support

Cancer is an all-too common ailment in our day and age. While its causes vary and are often difficult to pinpoint, many sufferers have benefitted from increasing their intake of whole, unprocessed plant foods.

Specifically, the antioxidants found in various fruits, vegetables, whole grains, seeds, nuts, and legumes are believed to fight the spread of free-radicals—unstable particles in the body that can damage and mutate cell DNA, causing many of the issues related to cancer growth.

Though the free-radical/antioxidant theory is not conclusive, it does correspond with the idea that individuals can significantly improve their health by improving the way they eat. And while the NutriBullet does not claim to cure or alleviate the causes and/or symptoms of cancer—or any illness for that matter—it can be used as a powerful tool to maximize the amount of vegetables, fruits, and other wholesome foods in your diet.

PLEASE CONSULT YOUR DOCTOR BEFORE CHANGING YOUR DIET OR ENGAGING IN ANY OF THE AFOREMENTIONED ACTIVITIES, ESPECIALLY IF YOU HAVE BEEN DIAGNOSED OR ARE UNDERGOING TREATMENT FOR CANCER OR ANY OTHER ILLNESS. ADDITIONALLY, ANTIOXIDANT FOODS ARE SOMETIMES ADVISED AGAINST DURING CHEMOTHERAPY AND RADIATION. ASK YOUR DOCTOR FOR PERSONAL DIETARY RECOMMENDATIONS.

In addition to increasing antioxidant intake through food, there are a multitude of other habits believed to be beneficial for cancer prevention and recovery. These include:

Reducing or Eliminating Meat Consumption

Studies show that a plant-based diet may decrease cancer risk.

Decreasing Fat and Oil Intake

This refers especially to chemically processed fats and oils. Look at food labels before purchasing an item, and pass on any foods containing trans fats or hydrogenated oils.

Sweating

It is noted that sweating helps your body eliminate toxins that could potentially initiate cancer cell mutation. Engage in exercises that promote perspiration and/or sit in an infared sauna for 20-30 minutes a day, or at least as often as possible.

The contents of this book are meant for informational purposes only. Please consult your doctor before changing your diet or engaging in any of the aforementioned activities, especially if you have been diagnosed or are undergoing treatment for cancer or any other illness. Additionally, antioxidant foods are sometimes advised against during chemotherapy and radiation. Ask your doctor for personal dietary recommendations.

*This information is for informational purposes only.

NutriBullet
testimonials

" Shari P.

My quest for more energy, a strong immune system, and a healthy weight ended here…

I always thought that if I worked out, did not eat a lot of red meat and took vitamins that it meant that I was being proactive about my health. The problem was that I did not feel healthy. Like many people I got wrapped up in a hectic lifestyle and didn't pay attention to nutrition. The result was a slow metabolism, a lack of energy and a compromised immune system.

It never occurred to me that by making simple changes in how I consumed food, I could strengthen my immune system, lose weight, increase energy and improve my overall appearance.

It took a cancer diagnosis to make me realize that changes needed to be made in my diet. While I had the most amazing doctors who saved my life, none of them provided guidance as to what or how I should be eating in order to have enough energy to get through the treatment process, or how to build my immune system to prevent the cancer from returning.

Every bit of my research brought me back to something so basic: juicing whole fruits and vegetables was the best way to meet my goals.

I decided to purchase a juicer, but none of the juicers on the market appeared to be the right fit for my busy lifestyle and health goals. They were either too large, too time consuming to clean or too expensive. I wanted something that was simple to use and easy to clean so that I would make it a part of my daily routine and not have it end up in my cupboard after a week.

I came upon an opportunity to try the NutriBullet program. I was intrigued by the fact that the NutriBullet actually extracts the nutrients from fruits and vegetables, making them easier to digest so the nutrients would be better absorbed in the body.

Within one day of using my NutriBullet, changes were apparent. I had an infusion of energy and felt better than I had in years. After a week my face began to glow and my hair began to grow back from the chemotherapy at an extraordinary rate.

My goal now is to share my NutriBullet success story with others so that people can join me in my journey of recovery and good health. I am excited to share all of the wonderful things the NutriBullet and the program have to offer! "

Lori T.

http://nutribulletblog.com/share-your-story/#comment-9281

I was diagnosed with breast cancer in January 2012 and had a double mastectomy followed by radiation treatment in February. For 10 years before I was diagnosed, I'd had insomnia and used over-the-counter meds to help me sleep. With the added stress of my cancer diagnosis to my insomnia, I needed something stronger to help me sleep, so I went on prescription sleep aids. I knew I had to get off them eventually, but couldn't.

I saw your infomercial in August and decided to try the NutriBullet. I started reading your book as soon as my package arrived and headed to the store to buy cancer-fighting and sleep-assisting foods.

After 2 months with the NutriBullet, I finally got brave and went to bed without my prescription sleep aid. I fell asleep right away and slept all night. I've been sleeping well ever since.

As for my cancer, my blood work in August had 10 numbers that were not in range. In November, ALL of my numbers were in range. I have 2 NutriBlasts a day and I love them.

I feel GREAT!!! Thanks for this awesome product.

Pamela J.

I was diagnosed with throat cancer two years ago and had to have a stomach tube inserted while I was doing radiation. The treatments made it nearly impossible to swallow or to eat that much. With the Nutribullet I was able to make sure that I was getting all the nutrients my body needed to help me fight the effects of treatment and the nasty cancer.

What I was very worried about was the drastic weight loss I was suffering, so I made sure I loaded my Bullet up with plenty of greens to get all my vitamins and I always, every morning, made the Immune Blast, to help keep my immune system as healthy as possible. I followed that up with my second Blast of the day, the Vitamin Blast, to make sure I was getting all my daily vitamins. For those of you with a feeding tube, the NutriBullet grinds and blends everything to the perfect consistency—no plugged tubes. If your Blast seems a little thick, just add pure water to make it thinner.

I am glad to say the NutriBullet was my savior during the 12 weeks I was unable to swallow very well. When I finished treatment, every other morning I drank the Detox Blast to help clean out the effects of the treatments. I now feel like a new person. All of my checkups have been great!

I recommended the NutriBullet to everyone, whether they have an ailment or are just hoping to get over the Sick and Tired Syndrome they are suffering from.

" Ryn G.

http://nutribulletblog.com/share-your-story/#comment-8925

I am a 41 year-old cancer survivor. Since treatment, I had been suffering from a slew of health problems including a weakened immune system, anemia, and bad digestion. My hair was really fine, my nails were brittle, and the color in my face was dull. My energy was low and I was taking medication for all my symptoms.

A few months ago, much like everyone else, I watched the NutriBullet infomercial and decided to give it a try. I'm a healthy weight of 117 at 5'4, but was not getting all the nutrients and vitamins that I needed throughout the day, so I started by making two Blasts a day and eating one meal at night. I was amazed at how quickly my system changed. Within two to three weeks, my skin was fuller and glowing, I had more energy, and I could think more clearly. I haven't been sick since I started drinking these miracle green drinks.

Now that I'm getting the daily vitamins and fiber that my body needs, I'm no longer on medication for my digestive system and no longer anemic. I look forward to your liquid miracle drinks everyday and feel better everyday for drinking them.

I am so excited about the wonderful benefits that I have received from the NutriBullet, that I share the wealth of health with anyone I can. I work at a 55+ community and constantly answer questions about my green elixir!

I have also shared my experiences with my 65-year-old mother, who suffers from severe arthritis and has undergone surgeries for her hip, back, throat, and neck. After providing her with a few of my favorite recipes and a few that I thought would benefit her the most, she has fallen in love with the NutriBullet and all of the newfound energy it has given her. Her arthritis is not as severe, her aches and pains have diminished, she is no longer depressed, and she has started exercising more.

I want to thank you from the bottom of my heart for helping my mother, so many others, and me. "

Stacy G.

Special thanks from a cancer survivor!!

THANK YOU NutriBullet for giving me my fruits, veggies, energy and life back!! For almost 10 years, I have been denying my body the important nutrients that fruits and veggies provide. It was NOT my choice, but rather a situation that I was forced to have to deal with.

I am a cancer survivor. The effects of the surgeries that saved my life had a HUGE impact on me. I had a Hemicolectomy- a procedure that removed about 3 feet of my colon to prevent any further spreading of cancer cells from a very rare Carcinoid Tumor that had grown in my appendix. When you are alive and cancer free – giving up things such as particular foods is easy- you are just happy to have a life.

Now, almost 10 years later (and still cancer free), my body is dealing with the after-effects of not having proper nutrients. In my case I am not able to break down the foods that my body needs. The NutriBullet has given me back that ability and, in turn, has given me back a whole new world of possibilities of foods that have been on my 'naughty list' for a long time.

I can't thank you enough!!! This is more than a cute little machine that sits on my counter, this is a lifestyle now for me. I have energy, I can get through my day with a better sense of accomplishment, my skin is clear and my digestive tract is actually on track.

THANK YOU!!
Stacy

For more life changing stories, please visit NutriLiving.com

Cancer Prevention & Recovery Support
nutriblasts

Upping the Antioxidant

Hit the nutritional jackpot with this powerful NutriBlast!

- ½ cup fresh blueberries
- 5 fresh strawberries
- 1 to 2 cups kale (to fill NutriBullet **Tall cup** ¾ full)
- 1 Tbsp chia seeds
- water to the **MAX LINE**

Place all ingredients in the **Tall Cup** and **extract** for 30-45 seconds.

Shades of Grape

Red grapes are celebrated for their high concentration of resveratrol—a powerful antioxidant that has been linked to inhibited cancer cell growth. Combine with spinach, green tea, and pecans, and you've got yourself one guiltless pleasure!

- 1 cup red grapes, purple grapes, or a combination of both (preferably with seeds)
- 1 to 2 cups spinach (to fill NutriBullet **Tall cup** ¾ full)
- 1 cup brewed green tea (chilled)
- 2 Tbsp chopped pecans
- water to the **MAX LINE**

Place all ingredients in the **Tall Cup** and **extract** for 30-45 seconds.

Red Handed

Get caught with this ruby-colored concoction and give your body a hearty dose of vitamin C and carotenoid antioxidants!

- 1 sliced red bell pepper, stem and core removed
- ½ cup raspberries
- ½ cup strawberries
- ½ frozen banana
- 1-2 cups arugula
- 10 almonds
- water to the **MAX LINE**

Place all ingredients in the **Tall Cup** and **extract** for 30-45 seconds.

Cherry On Top

This bright juicy concoction is bursting with flavorful, free radical stabilizing cherries. Broccoli and flax up the antioxidant content, while ginger eases nausea for those undergoing treatment. Make your Blast extra frosty by using frozen organic cherries!

- 1 cup cherries, pits removed
- ½ cup broccoli florets
- 1-2 cups mixed greens
- 1 ½-inch piece of ginger
- 1 Tbsp chia seed
- water to the **MAX LINE**

Place all ingredients in the **Tall Cup** and **extract** for 45-50 seconds.

Cancer Prevention & Recovery Support
meals & snacks

Luscious Black Lentil Soup

Yields 6 servings

This delicious and hearty dish is perfect for lunch or dinner. While all lentils are healthful, the black variety contains the highest levels of anthocyanin antioxidants of any type. In addition to the tiny legumes, this soup features a wide variety of nutrient dense veggies and spices to nourish your body from the inside out!

- 3 cups vegetable stock
- 2 cups water
- 2 small onions, chopped
- 4 garlic cloves, minced
- 4 tomatoes, roughly chopped
- 1 teaspoon turmeric
- 2 teaspoons ground cumin
- 1 tsp ground cardamom
- 1 small cinnamon stick (or half a large one)
- 1 1/3 cups dried black lentils (also known as beluga lentils)
- 1 tablespoon lime juice (about half a lime)
- salt and pepper
- cumin seeds to garnish

Bring water, vegetable stock, onions, garlic, tomatoes, turmeric, ground cumin, cardamom, cinnamon, and lentils to boil in a large pot over high heat. Reduce heat to medium, cover, and let simmer for 25 minutes.

Turn off the heat, remove the cinnamon stick, and allow to completely cool to room temperature, about 1 hour. You can speed this process up by refrigerating the pot after cooking.

Pour portions of the soup into the **Tall Cup** to ½ full and pulse with the **Extractor Blade** two to three times until lentils are loosely broken, but still solid. Pour the extracted soup into a second pot. Reheat over medium heat for another 5-10 minutes, stirring in lime juice and seasoning with salt and pepper until warm.

Enjoy!

Chocolate Chia Pudding

Makes 4 Servings

Chia seeds are loaded with fiber, omega-3 fatty acids, and free radical-stabilizing antioxidants. Steep them in homemade almond date milk and raw cacao, and watch them transform from humble seed to silky smooth dessert! Who knew decadence could be this healthful?

- 1/4 cup chia seeds
- 1/2 cup raw almonds, soaked in water overnight, skins removed
- 4 pitted medjool dates, soaked in water overnight
- 2 cups water
- 1 Tbsp raw cacao powder
- pinch of sea salt
- ¼ tsp ground cinnamon
- 1 Tbsp coconut butter
- 2 tsp pure vanilla extract

Prepare almonds and dates the night before making your pudding.

Place chia seeds in a medium-sized mixing bowl and set aside.

Add skinned soaked almonds, water, cacao, dates, salt, cinnamon, coconut butter, and vanilla extract to the **Tall Cup**. **Extract** with the **Extractor Blade** in 1-minute intervals, resting 1 minute between each extraction (this should take no more than 3 extractions).

Pour liquid over the chia seeds and whisk thoroughly to mix ingredients. Let the mixture sit for 15 minutes, whisking every few minutes to ensure a clump-free pudding.

Refrigerate for 4 hours before serving.

Shari's Apple Spice Pie Blast

This delicious dessert Blast, concocted by cancer survivor and NutriBullet enthusiast Shari Pack, will satisfy your sweet tooth without the negative consequences! Antioxidant-rich berries, filling oats, blood sugar-regulating cinnamon, and walnuts packed with omega-3 fatty acids all combine to give you a healthfully decadent treat!

- 1 apple
- 1 handful(s) blueberries
- 1 cup(s) unsweetened almond milk
- cup(s) oats
- ½ tsp cinnamon
- 5 Walnuts
- 1 tsp chia seeds
- ice
- 1 pinch nutmeg, to garnish

Add all ingredients except the nutmeg to your **Tall Cup** and **extract** for 30 seconds. Garnish with nutmeg.

Blast Away the
pounds!

The safe, healthy way to lose weight
keep it off *AND improve your overall health!*

As much as we wish it were so, there's no one magic food to eat or avoid to drop pounds. Losing weight is not an isolated task; it requires an overall lifestyle change that incorporates food choices, portion size, physical activity, and stress reduction. Over time, daily changes in a person's approach to nutrition and exercise will translate into lost inches.

The foods in the following NutriBlasts, meals, and snacks are high in fiber, water, and nutrients, and low in calories. These foods—mostly vegetables and whole grains—will fill you up, maximize your nutritional intake, stabilize your blood sugar, and boost your metabolism. Low-glycemic fruits like berries and apples also make appearances, as well as small portions of healthy fats and protein, which increase satiety—leaving you more satisfied with your meal and less likely to overeat.

In addition to the aforementioned dietary changes, here are a few other tips and tricks to get you started on your weight loss journey.

Smart Start

Skip the snooze button and get a move on! Starting the day with moderate exercise can kickstart your metabolism, increasing the rate at which you burn energy throughout the day. If you want to boost your metabolic rate even further, enjoy one of these beverages at least half an hour before breakfast:

> Cold water with lemon
> Herbal Tea with lemon
> 16 ounces of water mixed with 1 Tbsp apple cider vinegar

Team Spirulina

Spirulina, a blue-green variety of algae, is full of protein and GLA (gamma-linolenic acid)—a healthy omega-6 fatty acid shown to assist in weight loss. You can find spirulina in capsule or powder form at most health food stores. Add either form to your NutriBlast, or take the capsule as a supplement.

Lab = Flab

Processed and refined foods provide ample calories with little nutritional value. Relying on them as a substantial part of your diet can lead to weight gain and malnourishment—yes, it is possible to be overweight and malnourished!

Be wary of any packaged foods (even if they claim to be "all-natural" or "organic"), and check out the ingredient label before purchasing. If it contains more than five ingredients, unpronounceable terms, or any other indication that it was compiled in a laboratory instead of grown from the ground, leave it on the shelf.

PLEASE CONSULT A PHYSICIAN OR HEALTHCARE PROFESSIONAL BEFORE CHANGING YOUR DIET OR ENGAGING IN ANY OF THE AFOREMENTIONED CONDITIONS, ESPECIALLY IF YOU ARE PREGNANT, NURSING, OR UNDERGOING TREATMENT/TAKING MEDICATION FOR A SPECIFIC MEDICAL CONDITION.

Weight Loss
testimonials

The NutriBullet is a wonderful companion to your weight loss goals, as it allows for quick, clean preparation of some of the world's most nutritious and satisfying foods. Here are a few real-life examples of people who have lost weight and increased their overall quality of life by incorporating the NutriBullet into their daily routine!

" Daniel A.

http://www.nutriliving.com/articles/weight-loss-and-fatty-liver-0
I bought my NutriBullet on August 10th, 2012.

I weighed 193 lbs with high cholesterol and a fatty liver. I was also suffering from IBS (Irritable Bowel Syndrome) and GERD (Gastroesophageal Reflux Disease). I was up late one night, not asleep because of stomach pains, when I saw the NutriBullet infomercial.

I usually ignore things that have to do with weight loss or health, because they are usually trying to push some type of powder, pill or fad diet, but this was different. It made a lot more sense than anything else; we already know that eating vegetables and fruits is healthy for us, but we really don't want to take the time to purchase or prepare them when we can much more easily drive up to a fast food chain and grab a double cheeseburger and fries.

After watching the infomercials, I figured I would do more research before making my purchase and I found a lot of great blenders, but they cost between $300-$500. I could have waited, but I probably would have lost interest in getting healthy. The next day, I searched for stores that had them in stock and I spent around $100. Once I got home, I threw in some spinach, bananas, strawberries, and almond milk and made a great Blast. I kept doing this for several days every morning and I felt great. So great, in fact, that I decided to research other foods that I could extract for health.

As days went by, I started to lose weight from just the Blasts. With the knowledge I had gained, I started making substitutions in what I ate, such as a simple swap of quinoa for rice and even quinoa pastas for regular pastas. I noticed that I was able to stop using my Nexium

for reflux and that I no longer had headaches or stomachaches. After a month, I had lost 20 lbs, felt great, and noticed my clothes fit better. I continued to want to improve myself.

During this change in my life, family members and coworkers started seeing the changes in my skin, body, and attitude, and it was infectious. People all around me have started making small changes, even buying NutriBullets for themselves.

After my 7th week, I decided it was time to go back to my doctor and have a check-up and blood work done. He was amazed at my weight loss and asked me about my dietary habits—he even asked my advice and opinions on things. They took my blood and found that I had lowered my cholesterol to 161 and my enzyme counts had lowered as well, reflecting the shape of my fatty liver. I intend to return 2 months from now and have completely healthy liver function.

Throughout this whole process, I have focused on being healthy, both for myself and for my family. I want to be a great role model for my son who is just 5 months old. I want him to know that food and health matter. If it wasn't for the NutriBullet, I would have not made all the efforts I have, so thank you so much for this product!

It has touched my life in more ways than I can explain!

" Karen P.

After juicing with a regular juicer, wasting pulp and feeling like I was throwing money away, I bought a NutriBullet. I had seen the infomercials late at night and bought one on sale at Kohl's. It has changed my life.

I have fibromyalgia. Since I have been making my NutriBlast drinks I feel so much better. I don't have as much inflammation as I used to and I don't have as much pain. I knew I needed to lose some weight, too, and wasn't sure how much I could lose having NutriBlasts. I lost 16.5 pounds within 3 weeks. I have continued to lose weight and am now down 2.5 sizes in clothes. I feel GREAT! I have a lot more energy now, too!

Jonathan B.

WOW. I am using the NutriBullet with my favorite fruits and veggies to create very good NUTRIBLASTs, and the concept cannot be simpler: 50% green leafs + 50% fruit and veggies + boost + water.

I was a big eater, weighing a little over 300 pounds at the end of my 30 s. I realized that I needed to get in shape before it was too late.

Here I am 2 weeks later, 15 pounds lighter.

For now, my best friend and ally is my NutriBullet system and the NATURAL HEALING FOODS BOOK.

Amber

I have been married 24 years. We have both put on weight, but my husband went a little overboard and now he is obese. I'm always looking for something to get us on the right track (Weight Watchers, Atkins, Medifast, etc.), but nothing seems to stick.

I saw the infomercial for the NutriBullet and we thought, "why not?" We got the pretty box home, took everything out, looked over the booklets and let it sit in our cupboard for a few months.

I stumbled across the commercial again and thought "What is wrong with us? Get that thing running!"

We started at the end of March and haven't looked back! I'm down 11 lbs and hubby is down 13lbs. We feel great, sleep better and it's so easy! Every morning I make a Blast and after a healthy dinner, I make a dessert Blast! Best of all?! This seems to be "IT" for my hubby!

I'm so excited to see what the Bullet future holds for us! Thank you NutriBullet!

Clara A.

I have been overweight all my 26 years of life. I decided to do something about it and began running in 2010. Some of the weight came off, but then I plateaued. Somehow, I was still tired all the time (working 12-hour shifts as a nurse left me drained). I had insomnia, anxiety, bad acne, joint pain, horrible migraines and a thyroid hormone level that was all over the place.

In January 2013, I decided to focus on my nutrition. I began eating healthier and drinking more water and, after seeing the amazing runner Nadia Ruiz use the NutriBullet, I decided to give it a try.

At first, my body began detoxing, and as the days progressed I started noticing a difference. Since then, I have lost 25 lbs. I sleep better, my thyroid level is normal, my skin is clearing up, my headaches are gone, and I feel more energized.

Before, I would have to drink 5 cups of coffee a day to survive a 12-hour shift. Now I drink 1 cup, sometimes none. I have more energy at the hospital and more energy while working out. To me, that's amazing!!!

One of the best things about the NutriBullet is that starting your day with a Blast in the morning gets you eating healthier the entire day. It gets you used to making healthier food and activity choices, something that I am very grateful for!

I find myself in the grocery store buying organic fruits/veggies, looking for Acai/Goji berries and researching the healthiest foods out there. Last year, I completed a marathon in 7.5 hours. This year it took me 6.5 hours and I can definitely attribute this to healthy eating and the NutriBullet. I have cut down ten minutes in my half-marathon time. I can run better and recover faster with the NutriBullet.

THANK YOU, NUTRIBULLET! I cannot wait to see my health improve (and my running pace improve) in the future months.

Weight Loss
nutriblasts

iZenny's Green Food Lover's Blast

This tasty green elixir was inspired by NutriLiving.com user IZenny, who posted a similar recipe that's "perfect for green food lovers who perhaps, like me, want their NutriBlast tasty but not overly sweet...It's great for weight loss, (and) packed full of long-lasting energy, fiber, and vital nutrients."

- ¼ cucumber, sliced
- ¼ zucchini, sliced
- 1 celery stalk
- ½ cup fresh pineapple
- 1 large handful of chopped kale
- 1 large handful of spinach
- 1 large handful of fresh parsley
- 1 Tbsp chia seeds
- 1 tsp maca powder
- 1 cup unsweetened coconut water (optional)
- water to the **MAX LINE**

Add all ingredients to the **Tall Cup** and **extract** until smooth.

PLEASE CONSULT YOUR DOCTOR BEFORE CHANGING YOUR DIET OR ENGAGING IN ANY OF THE AFOREMENTIONED ACTIVITIES, ESPECIALLY IF YOU HAVE BEEN DIAGNOSED OR ARE UNDERGOING TREATMENT FOR CANCER OR ANY OTHER ILLNESS. ADDITIONALLY, ANTIOXIDANT FOODS ARE SOMETIMES ADVISED AGAINST DURING CHEMOTHERAPY AND RADIATION. ASK YOUR DOCTOR FOR PERSONAL DIETARY RECOMMENDATIONS.

Melon Out

Melon adds a ton of flavor to your NutriBlasts, but contains less sugar and calories than other sweet fruits. Full of beta-carotene, vitamins A and C and antioxidants, this Blast not only helps you manage your weight, but also contributes to healthy lungs, improved immunity, and overall well-being. This Blast's cool and sweet flavors are especially refreshing on a hot day.

- 2 handfuls spinach
- ½ cup cantaloupe
- ½ cup honeydew
- ½ cup watermelon
- 1 Tbsp goji berries
- ½ stalk celery
- juice of 1 lime
- water to the **MAX LINE**

Add all ingredients to the **Tall Cup** and **extract** until smooth (about 25 seconds).

Slimming Citrus

Brimming with low-glycemic citrus and berries, this Blast is juicy and sweet without the blood sugar-spiking qualities of other fruits.

- 2 cups spinach
- ¼ grapefruit
- ½ orange
- 3 strawberries
- ½ cup of raspberries
- 1 Tbsp chia seeds
- water to the **MAX LINE**

Add all ingredients to the **Tall Cup** and **extract** until smooth (about 45 seconds).

Pounds Down

Don't go out and buy bottled vegetable juice; this fresh and easy recipe is far tastier and far better for you! It's light, but filling, with a touch of spice to boost your metabolism. Plus, these fruits and veggies are low glycemic, making this recipe a perfect companion to your weight loss goals!

- 2 cups spinach
- 1 large tomato
- ½ stalk celery
- ½ carrot
- ½ bell pepper
- ¼ small yellow or white onion
- juice from ½ lime
- 2 sprigs cilantro
- 1 to 2 cups water (to fill NutriBullet **Tall cup** halfway)

Add all ingredients to the **Tall Cup** and **extract** until smooth (about 45 seconds).

Weight Loss
meals & snacks

Grainy Day Salad
Serves 6-8

This delicious, filling dish can be made with whatever unprocessed whole grain you happen to have in the pantry—quinoa, brown rice, barley, wheatberries, even steel-cut oats! White beans and artichokes add flavor, depth, fiber, and minerals to nourish and satisfy your shrinking belly!

- 4 cups cooked quinoa, brown rice, or other whole grain
- the hearts of 4 steamed artichokes, chopped, or 1 14-oz can organic artichoke hearts, rinsed, drained, and chopped
- 1 ½ cups cooked white beans, such as navy, Great Northern or cannellini (can be home-cooked or canned)—rinsed and drained
- ¾ cup chopped fresh parsley
- ½ small red onion, finely diced
- 1 red bell pepper, diced
- 1 small cucumber, peeled and diced
- 1 Tbsp fresh dill
- Juice of 2 lemons
- 2 tablespoons extra-virgin olive oil
- ½ tsp sea salt
- ¼ tsp black pepper (preferably fresh ground)
- additional salt and pepper to taste

Cook grains, as well as artichokes and beans (if not using the canned variety).

Combine cooked grains, artichokes, beans, parsley, onion, pepper, and cucumber in a large bowl.

In the **Tall Cup**, **extract** lemon juice, olive oil, salt, and pepper. Pour over the grain mixture and stir ingredients until well combined. Season with extra salt and pepper to taste.

Note: If you are in a rush with no time to chew, divide ingredients by 4, extract in the NutriBullet, and drink this salad as a Blast!

Miso-Glazed Salmon with Broccoli Soba Noodles

Serves 4

Japanese ingredients put a tasty spin on a classic dinner combination. Most grocery stores now carry ingredients like miso and soba noodles, but if you live in a more rural area, both ingredients can be purchased at health food stores or online. Soba noodles can be prepared in advance, refrigerated, reheated, or served cold for a speedy weeknight dinner.

Broccoli Soba Noodles

Soba noodles cook much faster than Italian pastas. Make sure to pay attention while they boil to avoid overcooking. Soba noodles also contain gluten, so those with gluten allergies/intolerance can substitute brown rice noodles.

- 8 ounces dried soba noodles
- 2 – 3 cups chopped broccoli florets
- zest of one lemon
- 1 cup fresh cilantro, chopped
- 2 large cloves garlic
- 3 Tbsp toasted sesame oil
- 3 Tbsp organic, unsweetened apple juice
- 1 Tbsp apple cider vinegar
- 1/4 teaspoon cayenne powder
- 1/2 teaspoon fine grain sea salt

Bring a pot of salted water to boil. Add soba noodles and broccoli and cook 3 to 5 minutes. Drain the mixture, but do not rinse it.

Add the lemon zest, cilantro, garlic cloves, sesame oil, apple juice, and apple cider vinegar to the **Tall Cup** and pulse 4-5 times with the **Extractor Blade** until the mixture emulsifies.

Transfer noodles and broccoli to a large bowl and toss with the mixture until fully coated.

Salmon

- 1/2 cup white miso paste
- 2 Tbsp rice vinegar
- 1 Tbsp brown rice, or pure maple syrup
- One 1 ½ -inch piece of ginger, peeled
- 1 ½ tsp toasted sesame oil
- ½ tsp sesame seeds, plus another ½ tsp to garnish
- 4 5-oz salmon filets of even thickness

Preheat oven to 400 degrees.

Add miso, vinegar, sweetener, ginger, sesame oil, and ½ tsp sesame seeds to the **Tall Cup** and extract with the **Extractor Blade** until fully liquefied.

Arrange salmon in a shallow baking dish. Pour glaze over the salmon and bake for 15-20 minutes, opening the oven every 5 minutes to spoon the glaze over the filets.

Roasted Grapefruit with Pistachio Cream

Makes 4 Servings

Unique flavor, color, and texture combinations give this elegant dessert a decadent quality without any added guilt! It's also full of fiber and antioxidants, and low in calories (provided you don't overdo the pistachio cream)—the perfect nightcap to your day of healthy eating! The pistachio cream requires some time for soaking and refrigeration, so we recommend making it up to 24 hours before serving the dessert.

Pistachio Cream

- 1/3 cup shelled pistachios, soaked for at least 4 hours
- 1 tbsp brown rice or maple syrup OR raw honey
- 1/4 cup water or coconut water
- 1/2 avocado, pit and skin removed
- 1/2 teaspoon lemon juice
- 1 pinch sea salt
- extra chopped pistachios, to garnish

Drain the pistachios and add all ingredients to the **Tall Cup**. **Extract** for 20-30 seconds until the mixture is smooth and fluffy, with small flecks of pistachios evenly distributed throughout. You may need to unscrew the blade, redistribute the ingredients, and **extract** again to ensure an even texture. Refrigerate for at least 1 hour before serving.

Roasted Grapefruit

- 2 grapefruits, halved and arranged on a parchment-lined baking sheet
- 1-2 tsp cinnamon

When ready to prepare, preheat oven to 400 degrees.

Sprinkle cinnamon over grapefruit halves and bake for 15 minutes until just browned (be careful not to burn, as the fruit's sugars will caramelize suddenly. ·

Allow to cool for 10 minutes, then top with 2 Tbsp pistachio cream each.

For more weight loss recipes,
please visit NutriLiving.com

Dominate
diabetes!

Prevent and manage Type 2 Diabetes through extracted nutrition

Diabetes is one of the most prevalent health problems in America today. The disorder is categorized by the body's inability to manufacture or process insulin—a hormone that plays a hugely important role in the regulation of blood sugar and the energy it provides.

There are two main categories of diabetes: Type 1, which develops in childhood and results from the pancreas' inability to manufacture insulin, and the more common Type 2 diabetes, which generally emerges in adulthood (though is becoming increasingly prevalent in children) and involves the body's inability to effectively use the insulin that the pancreas manufactures. While Type 1 diabetes usually results from damage to the pancreas, Type 2 diabetes is strongly linked to dietary and lifestyle choices.

Many type 2 diabetics and pre-diabetics have benefitted from a change in their dietary habits. Because their bodies' ability to regulate glucose levels is compromised, diabetics much take extra care in deciding what to eat, when to eat, and how much to eat.

While a dietician is the best source for specific dietary advice, it is widely accepted that eliminating processed food from the diet, choosing whole grains over refined grains, limiting sugar intake (especially refined sugar intake), and increasing dietary fiber intake are basic changes diabetics and pre-diabetics can make to improve their health.

The NutriBullet makes an excellent tool for those diagnosed with diabetes, because it allows its users to easily eat and absorb a wide variety of high-fiber, nutrient-dense vegetables and low-glycemic fruits, as well as plant based fats and proteins that slow the release of sugar into the blood. And when you start feeding your body better, you will feel better from the inside out!

In addition to replacing processed foods with fruits, vegetables, and whole grains, and incorporating NutriBlasts into your daily diet, here are a few other bits of information that can help you maintain balanced blood sugar and regulate your diabetes.

Spice, Spice Baby

Studies show that cinnamon can enhance the body's ability to utilize insulin and stabilize blood sugar levels.

Get a Move On

Exercise is excellent for those with diabetes*, as it lowers blood sugar levels and improves circulation. If you are not a regular exerciser, start by incorporating half-hour walks into your daily routine, and grow from there.

*Always monitor your blood sugar levels before and after exercise if you have been diagnosed with Diabetes.

Still Sweet

Craving something sugary, but worried about your glucose levels? Try using stevia extract instead of sugar, honey, or other high-glycemic sweeteners. Stevia extract is all-natural, plant-based, and free of calories or chemicals that can upset blood sugar levels.

Diabetes
testimonials

" ## Dan P.

I have spent years trying all kinds of diet combinations, exercise and supplements to control my diabetes. I was using 46 units of Lantis insulin every night when I changed to a plant-based, mostly raw and organic diet and my blood sugars started to drop. My doctor never prescribed this or even mentioned that I could control my diabetes this well with nutrition; he just told me to exercise and watch what I ate. The diet changes got me off of my cholesterol medicine and down to 8 units of insulin, but it was frustrating to come so far and still have to take that shot every night, plus the pill for my blood pressure. My mother-in-law asked if I wanted a NutriBullet for Christmas; I guess she saw the infomercial on TV and I thought it sounded a lot better than some of the gifts she's bought me over the years, so I said it would be great.

Well, I have to say, adding the NutriBlasts to my routine at Christmas was just the boost I needed to drop the last 8 units of insulin and the pill for my blood pressure. It's been 41 days since I stopped taking Lantis insulin and I've never had such good blood sugar readings or felt so energetic.

Aaron A.

On December 12, 2012, I was diagnosed as pre-diabetic. My cholesterol was through the roof, my hemoglobin at 5.8%. As General Patton said, "Always take the offensive; never dig in," so with that in mind, I mounted an attack by way of diet and exercise, not giving it a chance to take me like it did my Grandpa and Uncle.

I tried the NutriBullet for the first time on February 25 – 28. I had the Beet Treat and Flex Factor as replacements for meals and by the fourth day, I was able to wake up with the energy I had when I was in high school. My taste buds felt like they were altered because beer wasn't appealing at my uncle's BBQ that weekend on March 2.

I knew I had something here, so I came up with a plan for April: "Operation Liquifaction." I picked eight of my favorites and got ready. I had drinks for breakfast and lunch, and salads with some fish for dinner right down to April 19 for my lab appointment, and April 26 for my follow-up with my doctor.

Here are my results:

My weight dropped from 211 lbs to 198.
My cholesterol was 236; now it's 180 (normal range is 125-200).

My LDL was at 148; now, 111 (LDL range should be 130).
Non-HDL was high at 199, now normal at 150.
My Triglycerides should be 150. They were 245, now 193. Still high, but a huge drop.
Ratio is still high at 6.0 (should be 5.0), but down from 6.4.

I'm 36 years old at 5'9 . My hemoglobin is still in the range of pre-diabetic at 5.7%, but that's the border. No meds required. My goal is to hit 180 pounds by this time next year, but I'll reach that by my trip to Maui this year in December. My doctor was really impressed: in her words, "Whatever you're doing, keep it up."

Lorrie C

Thank You NutriBullet!!! I couldn't be happier!!! I now have a way to make my food digestible, and my Type II diabetes is finally under control. I have so much energy; I wake up ready for anything.

I have had my NutriBullet for three weeks. I have been able to cut my insulin intake in half and my blood sugar is in now the 80 s. I expect that in not too much more time I may be off insulin all together!

My irritable bowel syndrome in totally under control and my food allergies are not giving me so many problems. I am able to eat so many more foods. I no longer feel like I am starving. I am actually losing weight, which was impossible to do since going on insulin. I have lost seven lbs. in 2 weeks. The insulin made me gain a lot of weight. I also have leaky gut syndrome. The Blasts are just the right consistency so that I am sure no more foods and bacteria are leaking into my blood stream.

I had just told my husband that if only I could make my food liquid, I was sure I would be able to digest it and not be in so much pain and bloated all of the time. A few days later he called me into the T.V. room to have me watch a commercial about the NutriBullet because he was sure it would be valuable to me. I didn't finish watching, I went directly to the phone and called and ordered one. We never order anything from the T.V., but I just knew I had to have one. I was so right. I can't thank NutriBullet enough.

My husband has had Type I diabetes for 23 years. He drinks the blasts, too. His blood sugar is improving and he has also been able to decrease his daytime insulin and has stopped his nighttime insulin all together. We tell everyone about the NutriBullet.

I am especially thankful because my husband has terminal cancer and I now feel that I will have the good health and energy to be his loving caretaker. Thanks, again, Nutribullet.

Blood Sugar Stabilizing
nutriblasts

Many diabetics wonder if it's okay for them to drink NutriBlasts - fruits do contain natural sugars, after all. But not to worry! We've got some tasty insulin-regulating Blasts that will help keep your blood sugar levels in check!

Blood Sugar Daddy

Embrace the nutritional gifts this Blast bestows! Cinnamon is a superboost known for its insulin-regulating powers, and the apple in this recipe makes your Blast sweet enough for your tastebuds, but not too sweet for your health.

- ½ **Tall Cup** Swiss Chard
- ½ apple
- ½ banana
- ¼ cup(s) pumpkin seeds
- 10 walnut halves
- 2 tsp cinnamon
- water to the **MAX LINE**

Add all ingredients to the **Tall Cup** and **extract** until smooth (about 25 seconds).

RawBerry Tart

Serves 6

- 2 cups almonds
- 1 cup rolled oats
- 1/2 cup sesame seeds
- 1 tsp salt
- 1 cup raisins, soaked for at least 4 hours
- 1/2 tsp vanilla extract
- 1 teaspoon cinnamon
- 1 pint fresh blackberries
- 1 pint fresh strawberries
- 2 tbsp lemon juice

Add almonds, rolled oats, sesame seeds, and salt to the **Tall Cup** and extract in quick pulses, shaking the cup in between to make sure all ingredients are evenly mixed, until mixture forms a flour-like consistency. Be careful not to over-extract, or the mixture will become more of a nut butter than a flour.

Add soaked raisins, vanilla extract, and cinnamon to another **Tall Cup** and extract in quick pulses until the fruit forms a sticky paste.

Add the oat/almond/sesame mixture and the raisin paste to a large bowl. Knead by hand to form an evenly-mixed dough. If you find the mixture is too crumbly, add water by the tablespoon until the mixture is moist enough to stick together, but firm enough to hold its own shape. Cover and refrigerate for 1 hour.

While the dough chills, rinse and dry blackberries and strawberries. Trim the stems off of the strawberries and slice into quarters. Add sliced strawberries and blackberries to a medium bowl, and stir in lemon juice. Set in the fridge alongside the dough.

Remove the dough from the refrigerator and press into the sides of a tart pan or similar container so it forms an even crust. Pour the lemon-juice soaked berries over the crust and arrange in an even layer. Refrigerate for an additional hour before serving.

For more blood sugar stabilizing recipes, please visit NutriLiving.com

Tips and Tricks For
an energetic you

Cut it Out

Eliminating certain foods from your diet can have a huge impact on your overall health. Common foods that reduce energy and increase symptoms of Fibromyalgia include fake colorings, caffeine, artificial sweeteners and preservatives. Some may notice a change in their pain levels when they stop eating dairy or gluten.

Inflammatory Statement

Certain foods have been shown to fight inflammation. Omega 3 Fatty Acids are powerful anti-inflammatories, so up your intake of hemp seeds, sardines, wild salmon, flax seed, chia seed, and walnuts. Other anti-inflammatory foods include ginger, turmeric, chili pepper, raw cacao and non-GMO soy.

High Frequency

Eating several small meals throughout the day has been shown to balance blood sugar and increase energy levels better than the standard 3-meal-a-day model. Try to eat 4-5 times a day, but be sure to watch your portion size and limit mini meals to 250-400 calories.

Sipping Pretty

Blasting with your NutriBullet helps unlock nutrients in your food that chewing alone cannot. This promotes maximum nutrient absorption within your system, which, in turn, supplies you with maximum energy.

PLEASE CONSULT A PHYSICIAN OR HEALTHCARE PROFESSIONAL BEFORE CHANGING YOUR DIET OR ENGAGING IN ANY OF THE AFOREMENTIONED CONDITIONS, ESPECIALLY IF YOU ARE PREGNANT, NURSING, OR UNDERGOING TREATMENT/TAKING MEDICATION FOR A SPECIFIC MEDICAL CONDITION.

Energy, Fibromyalgia, and inflammation
testimonials

> " **Island Girl**

It's been 6 weeks today since I bought my NutiBullet, and my life has changed so much for the better! I am extremely grateful for this amazing product, the NutriLiving Blog, and the wealth of health information it offers (I especially love the videos).

I'm almost 50 and have suffered from Chronic Fatigue Syndrome and Fibromyalgia for the past 7 years. After years of doctors' visits and ineffective medications and their negative side effects, I was feeling pretty hopeless and desperate to feel better again.

With my extreme exhaustion, brain fog, insomnia, and pain, I was bed-bound 50% of the time. My quality of life was as poor as my nutrition.

When I got my NutriBullet, I started by making small Blasts for the first few days, increasing to one large Blast per day by the end of the week. During week two, I had two large Blasts a day to replace breakfast and lunch. During the third week, I just listened to my body; it was begging for more NutriBlasts!

I decided to go on my own Blast Fast using only raw fruits and veggies, nuts, ground flax seeds, goji berries, maca powder, cacao powder, whey protein powder, and lots of water. I felt so good after one day that I wanted to continue. My Blast Fast lasted four and a half days!!! Holy maca!

I thought how I was feeling physically was just TOO good to be true! Losing two lbs during the Fast was an added bonus.

I literally ate/drank more fruits and vegetables in ONE week than I had in the past decade! Fruits and veggies were just never my thing, but they are now!

Here are some of the incredible results I've experienced so far using the NB:

-More Energy!

-Improved mood

-No more junk food cravings! My pantry isn't full of chips, cookies, canned vegetables, and other junk anymore; it's reserved for my healthy NutriBullet boosts and superfoods.

-No afternoon shakiness, or jitters from skipping breakfast & drinking six cups of coffee! I'm down to just one cup a day-Yay!

-Shinier, stronger hair

-Dry, itchy scalp-gone!

-Less Dry Eye-don't need eye drops everyday

-Patch of eczema on face disappeared!

-Less joint pain

-Normal regular bathroom visits

-Heightened mental clarity

-Libido change-from absolutely zero, none, nadda, to- wow, just wow! hahaha!

-Stopped bronchitis and sinusitis dead in its tracks!! I didn't even have to take the antibiotic my doctor gave me!

I just have to say- Thank You, Thank You, Thank You NURTIBULLET for creating this miraculous lifestyle changer to help people repair & heal themselves with good nutrition.

" Margie W.

I can't say enough about your product. It has TOTALLY changed my life!

I'm 56 years young and I have suffered with Rheumatoid Arthritis for 21 years. I have had four knee surgeries, a total elbow replacement and fusions in both of my wrists.

The RA really took a toll on my body and I was relying on 800 mg of Ibuprofen 3 times per day to help with my symptoms. The pain in my feet was so bad that every step felt like I was walking on sharp rocks. My feet were so inflamed that I was unable to wear close-toed shoes; I could only wear flip-flops. My right hand was also inflamed, so much that it was too painful to even hold my husband's hand.

When my Rheumatologist read my lab and x-ray reports in August, it didn't look good. She suggested I start taking steroids and methatrexate. Her advice was emotionally upsetting; I began to lose hope for my future.

When my husband and I saw the advertising of the NutriBullet, we decided to give it a try, even though we already had a VitaMix. As soon as the package arrived, I went on a 10 day juicing detox: NO FOOD, just NutriBlasts! Right away, I noticed that the inflammation in my feet and hands was disappearing! Each day it became easier for me to get out of bed and off the couch!

Now, I am walking without any pain—I'm not walking like I'm crippled anymore! My energy level has zoomed up and my mood swings are gone!

The NutriBullet is the most AMAZING product my husband and I have EVER bought!

I believe in your product so much that I share all of my recipes and pictures on Facebook. The response is INCREDIBLE! Many of my Facebook friends and family members have bought their own NutriBullets because of my posts! My husband, who is a nutritionist, also recommends your product to his clients.

There's nothing better than improving your health. Thanks to the NutriBullet, I haven't taken pain killers since August and I'm still INFLAMMATION/PAIN FREE!! I'm going back to my doctor next week and can't wait to show her how much my health has improved! I'm so very grateful for your product.

Thank you all again for making such a wonderful product! I will always be grateful!
-Margie (Mimi) "

Angel

My name is Angel and I am a NutriBullet believer. I have been suffering from chronic inflammation and pain in my neck and back (among other things) for years. That chronic pain and probably less-than-perfect diet had also taken a toll on me mentally and physically. I was so frustrated and afraid to do anything anymore because even nothing would make me hurt. I was treating myself with a handful of over-the-counter pain relievers every day to get a little relief, alternating them frequently to offset my body's increased tolerance against them. I took so many pain relievers daily that I built up tolerance quickly, so I had to alternate them frequently. A friend of mine one day told me that it sounded like I had fibromyalgia and suggested that I talk to my doctor.

The idea of re-explaining my invisible, phantom ailments to a doctor, and the time/expense of the tests I would have to take to find out if my problem was even treatable turned me off. Even if there were a treatment, it would just be more medication. Not interested.

My pain was so bad that I would wake up in bed from the pain. I felt like I had been hit by a bus—even on days that I slept through the night. No relief.

I was in desperation one morning and had seen the NutriBullet infomercial on TV. I figured nothing else was working and it sort of made sense to me. After reading so many reviews and watching testimonials, I bit the bullet (sorry for the pun) and bought one. I made a NutriBullet Blast religiously every morning.

Within one week, my inflammation was much better. Within two weeks, I was off pain relievers completely. Within three weeks, I discovered that my blood pressure was lower, heart rate was lower, and my cholesterol was lower by 14 points! I am amazed by these fast results! Before I used to do my morning NB Blasts, I just skipped breakfast altogether; it wasn't like I was substituting bacon and eggs for a Blast to explain the improvement in my vitals. I was feeling so good and had regained so much energy that I started running for fun by week four! I am still shocked about that. This is really working!

In addition to my largest complaint of pain/muscle inflammation, here are other things that improved since I have been Blasting: I feel calmer, my mood is better, my monthly female problems are almost non-existent, I sleep better (that literally happened overnight from the first day), and I feel more satisfied and have less cravings than before!

Inflammation Tamer

One of the roughest symptoms of fibromyalgia is chronic inflammation in the body, a condition that can lead to a host of other health problems. This Blast contains a wide variety of anti-inflammatory compounds to soothe your system.

- 2 big handfuls of spinach (enough to fill **Tall Cup** halfway)
- ½ cup blueberries
- ½ cup pineapple, cup into chunks
- 1 tsp maca root powder
- water to the **MAX LINE**

Add all ingredients to the **Tall Cup** and **extract** until smooth, about 40 seconds.

Limber Joint Libation

Arthritis pain is often caused by inflammation in the joints, which may be soothed by natural healing foods. Cherries, parsley, and turmeric are widely celebrated for their inflammation-fighting powers, so try this recipe if you suffer from the pains of arthritis and get your joints jumping once more!

- ½ **Tall Cup** spinach
- ½ cup cherries (pits removed)
- ½ cup pineapple
- ¼ cup parsley
- 1 Tbsp raw cacao (powder, nibs, or beans)
- 1 tsp turmeric
- water to **MAX LINE**

Add all ingredients to the **Tall Cup** and **extract** until smooth.

Energy-Boosting
meals & snacks

Curried Carrot Soup

Anti-inflammatory super foods ginger, turmeric, carrots, and lemon meld together to make this powerfully delicious soup!

- 2 tablespoons olive or coconut oil
- 1 teaspoon coriander seeds
- ½ teaspoon yellow mustard seeds
- ½ tsp cumin seeds
- ½ teaspoon turmeric
- ¼ tsp red chili powder (or more, depending on your spice preferences)
- 1 1-inch piece of ginger, peeled and minced
- 2 cloves of garlic, minced
- 2 onions, chopped
- 1 1/2 pounds carrots, peeled, thinly sliced into rounds (about 4 cups)
- 1 1/2 teaspoons lemon zest
- salt and pepper, to taste
- 4 cups low-sodium vegetable stock
- 2 cups coconut water
- 2 teaspoons fresh lemon juice

Heat oil in a large pot over medium heat. Add seeds, turmeric, and chili powder and stir for 1 minute to toast the seeds. Add ginger and cook for another minute.

Add garlic, onions, carrots, and lemon zest. Season with salt and pepper, and cook until onions and garlic soften—about 4 minutes.

Add the broth and coconut water and bring to a boil. Reduce heat to medium-low and simmer uncovered until carrots are cooked through, but not mushy—about half an hour.

Allow the soup to cool for an hour, or refrigerate for half an hour until it is room temperature, then stir in the lemon juice.

Add ¼ of the cooled vegetable/broth mixture to the **Tall Cup** and **extract** for 1-2 minutes until smooth, pausing every 45 seconds to avoid overheating. Transfer purée to a large bowl, and repeat the extracting process until all of the soup is puréed.

Store in the refrigerator for up to three days. Reheat on the stove before serving.

A Crust Above

Anti-inflammatory pizza is no pie in the sky idea. Get your inflammation-free pizza fix with our quinoa-based crust and dairy-free topping suggestions!

Crust

- 1 ½ cups quinoa, soaked overnight and drained
- ½ cup filtered water
- 1 tsp sea salt
- 3 Tbsp olive or cold-pressed virgin coconut oil, divided into two 1 ½ -tablespoon portions

Preheat your oven to 450 degrees.

Add the soaked quinoa, water, and salt to your **Tall Cup** and **extract** with the **Extractor Blade** until fully combined. Add more water if necessary—the prepared mixture should have the consistency of pancake batter.

Coat the base and sides of two 8-inch cake pans with the divided olive or coconut oil, and heat in the oven until the oil just starts to bubble. Remove from the oven and pour half of the crust batter into each pan. Bake for 20 minutes, then flip the crusts and bake an additional 10 minutes. Add toppings and enjoy!

Topping Suggestions:

Pesto

- 2 cups chopped kale leaves, spine removed
- 1 cup basil leaves
- 1/2 cup dry roasted almonds
- 4 large cloves of garlic
- 1/2 cup extra-virgin olive oil
- salt and pepper to taste

Add kale, basil, garlic and almonds to the **Tall Cup**.
Pulse mixture several times, unscrewing the top to scrape the sides of the cup, until all ingredients are finely minced.

Unscrew the blade, add half of the olive oil and pulse until oil is integrated. Add the remaining olive oil, salt and pepper, and **extract** until you reach desired consistency.

You can either spread this pesto on the fully cooked quinoa crust, or spread on top of the crust when you flip it over before baking an additional 10 minutes.

Tomato Basil with Cashew "Mozarella"

- 1 cup cashews, soaked overnight in water
- 2 garlic cloves
- juice from 1 lemon
- 1/2 tsp dijon mustard
- salt and pepper, to taste
- 2 Tbsp to ¼ cup Organic jarred tomato sauce (to taste)
- ½ tomato, thinly sliced
- 5-8 fresh basil leaves, rinsed

Preheat Broiler.

Add cashews, garlic, lemon juice, and mustard to the **Tall Cup** and **extract** in 50-second increments, pausing for 30 seconds in between each, until the mixture is smooth.

Spread tomato sauce on fully cooked quinoa crust, then spoon several dollops of cashew cheese on top to mimic the shape of mozzarella rounds. Top with tomato slices and basil leaves and heat under the broiler for 5 minutes, until the basil starts to shrivel and the other toppings are warm. Be sure to watch closely, as the herbs can burn quickly.

Walnut, Cherry, & Apple Crisp

- 2 medium apples
- 1 cup frozen organic pitted cherries (you can also use fresh cherries, just be sure to remove the pits!)
- ¼ cup maple syrup
- 1 Tbsp oat flour, plus ¼ cup for the topping
- 1 tsp lemon juice
- 1/2 tsp cinnamon
- 1 pinch of nutmeg
- ½ cup rolled oats
- ¼ cup palm or date sugar
- 3 Tbsp cold-pressed virgin coconut oil, plus an additional tablespoon to grease the pan
- ½ tsp vanilla extract

Preheat oven to 350 degrees. Grease a small baking dish with 1 Tbsp of coconut oil.

Remove apple cores and cut the fruit into ¼-inch slices. In a mixing bowl, combine the apples with cherries, maple syrup, 1 Tbsp oat flour, lemon juice, cinnamon and nutmeg. Mix thoroughly and transfer to the baking dish.

In another bowl add oats, 1/4 cup oat flour, sugar, 3 Tbsp coconut oil and vanilla.

Knead by hand until the mixture forms a crumbly consistency. Spread the topping evenly over the fruit layer.

Bake for 25-35 minutes, until the top is golden brown.

For more energy Boosting recipes,
please visit NutriLiving.com

Nutrition for mood
improvement *Blasting away the blues*

We all know a person's state of mind, or mood, can be greatly affected by external factors. Looming deadlines cause stress, issues in relationships cause anger or sadness, hearing good news can brighten a day; even the weather has an impact on how we feel! But how we feel is also dependent on internal factors—how our body is functioning, how we feel from the inside out.

It's no secret that what we eat can greatly impact our overall health and wellness. When we eat well, we help our body function efficiently, fueling us with the energy we need to take on the day. On the other hand, when we fail to give our bodies the nutrition it needs, we become sluggish and/or edgy. When we continuously function in a nutritionally devoid state, this sluggish and/or edgy feeling persists.

While chronic depression, anxiety, and other mood-related issues may stem from a wide variety of causes, diet has been shown to play a role in the severity of symptoms. Like with many health issues, eating a diet rich in plant-based vitamins and minerals can improve one's mood, while downing highly-processed, nutritionally-void "foods" can leave you feeling less than vibrant.

The following NutriBlast recipes highlight fruits, vegetables, and other plant-based foods that have been linked with improved mood. Some ingredients even contain chemical compounds that have been shown to trigger the release of good-mood neurotransmitters in the brain. But don't just take our word for it, find out for yourself!

IT IS IMPERATIVE THAT THOSE SUFFERING FROM ANY TYPE OF MOOD DISORDER NOT DISCONTINUE ANY MEDICATION WITHOUT FULL KNOWLEDGE OF A DOCTOR OR MENTAL HEALTHCARE PROFESSIONAL. DISCONTINUING THE USE OF MANY MOOD STABILIZERS, ANTI-DEPRESSANTS AND OTHER PSYCHO-PHARMACEUTICAL MEDICATIONS REQUIRES GRADUAL TAPERING DOWN TO AVOID REBOUND EFFECTS OR SIDE EFFECTS. DISCONTINUING SUCH MEDICATIONS CAN HAVE FATAL RESULTS.

PLEASE NOTE THAT PEOPLE SUFFERING FROM MOOD DISORDERS MAY BE MORE SENSITIVE TO DIETARY CHANGES, SO ANY MODIFICATIONS SHOULD BE GRADUAL. CERTAIN MEDICATIONS MAY REACT NEGATIVELY WHEN MIXED WITH CERTAIN FOODS, SO CONSULT YOUR DOCTOR OR MENTAL HEALTHCARE PROFESSIONAL BEFORE INCORPORATING ANY NEW FOOD OR SUPPLEMENT INTO YOUR DIET, ESPECIALLY IF YOU ARE TAKING MEDICATION FOR A MENTAL CONDITION OR ANY OTHER PHYSICAL AILMENT.

Mood Improvement
testimonials

" **Justin M.**

Hi, my name is Justin, and WOW!!! I am AMAZED by this machine!

Five years ago, I was diagnosed with chronic fatigue and panic disorders. I've been to countless doctors and tried supplements and medication. I even ended up in rehab for overdosing on Xanax because my anxiety was so bad.

I bought the NutriBullet system 3 months ago and it's like I'm a whole new person! I feel brand new. I have minimal to no anxiety, and I just feel more at peace. I feel like a kid again; I can do everything I couldn't do before.

Buying the NutriBullet was the best thing I ever did!! My friends and family ask me how I did it and I just tell them I bought the NutriBullet and drink two NutriBlasts a day. My friends Sammy and Carl bought the NutriBullet too, and they say they feel more energized and sleep better. It's great!

I'm really looking forward to the future now. Thank you so much for giving me my life back! "

Jim W.

I received my NutriBullet in the mail at the beginning of March 2013. At that time, I was pretty much at the end of my rope and didn't want to live anymore. I had suffered from severe depression for over 25 years. I tried every single antidepressant known to mankind. I had also tried direct current stimulation, transcranial magnetic stimulation, and ECT (shock therapy). Nothing ever worked. I was even considering having deep brain stimulation surgery!!

After seeing the NutriBullet infomercial on TV approximately 3 months ago, I decided to order one and give it a try. I thought I had nothing to lose.

At first I thought I was just imagining it, but I continued to have my NutriBlasts every day since then and have never felt better! The NutriBullet has completely changed my life! I've also lost a lot of weight and have so much energy now. Everyone has noticed my complete transformation!! I'm so thankful for your product; it's given me a new chance at life!!!
THANK YOU!!!

Mood Improving
nutriblasts

David Wolfe's Best Day Ever Blast

NutriBullet super food expert and all-around happy dude David Wolfe shares his recipe for the Best Day Ever!

- 1 banana
- 1 Tbsp raw cacao powder
- 1 small handful of goji berries
- 2 dollops of raw honey
- small chunk of aloe vera (outer skin removed)
- coconut water to the **MAX LINE**

Add all ingredients to the **Tall Cup** and **extract** for 45 seconds

Jim W's Brighter Days Blast

Inspired by Jim W.'s first NutriBlast, this recipe is loaded with Omega-3 fatty acids. Research suggests that increasing your Omega-3 intake may be one of the safest, easiest ways to combat depression.

- ¼ **Tall Cup** kale
- ¼ **Tall Cup** spinach
- ¼ cup blueberries
- 4 medium strawberries
- ½ banana
- ½ Tbsp flaxseed
- small handful of walnuts
- coconut water to the **MAX LINE**

Add all ingredients to the **Tall Cup** and **extract** until smooth (about 40 seconds).

Laura's Herbaceous Elation

This NutriBlast, adapted from NutriBullet Facebook fan Laura L., contains several mood-boosting ingredients: Swiss chard contains magnesium, a natural stress reliever, while basil contains eugenol and rosmarinic acid, compounds that boost the brain's production of dopamine and serotonin. Cinnamon and avocado are also happy ingredients; both help slow the release of glucose into the blood stream, calming blood sugar fluctuations that can often lead to agitation and irritability.

- 1/3 **Tall Cup** Swiss chard
- Handful of fresh basil (about 6 large leaves)
- 4 leaves fresh mint
- 1 fresh scallion, white part removed
- 1 cup strawberries
- 1 carrot, washed, peeled, and cut into rounds
- ½ avocado
- 2 tsp cinnamon
- unsweetened almond milk to the **MAX LINE**

Add all ingredients to the **Tall Cup** and **extract** until smooth (about 1 minute).

Mood Improving
meals & snacks

Artichoke and Barley Boost Bowl with Arugula Pesto
Makes 4-8 servings

Both the magnesium found in artichokes and the amino acid tryptophan found in barley help the brain manufacture serotonin—a neurotransmitter known for its mood-stabilizing and anxiety-soothing effects.

Barley and tomato sauce:
- 1 cup uncooked pearl barley, rinsed and drained
- 2 cups vegetable broth
- 1-2 Tbsp olive oil
- 2 cloves of garlic, thinly sliced
- 1 can water-packed organic artichoke hearts, rinsed and thoroughly drained
- 1 cup cherry tomatoes
- pinch of cayenne pepper to taste
- salt and pepper

Pesto:
- 2 cups fresh arugula
- ¼ cup fresh basil
- 1 clove garlic
- Juice from 1 lemon
- 1 Tbsp olive oil
- salt and pepper, to taste

In a medium-sized pot, add 2 cups vegetable broth to the barley and bring to a boil. Reduce heat and simmer for 30-40 minutes, until broth is absorbed and barley is fluffy and tender.

Add 1 Tbsp olive oil to a large saucepan over medium heat. Add sliced garlic and sauté until translucent—about 3 minutes. Add the artichokes and cook until both the garlic and artichokes are slightly browned—about 2-3 more minutes. Add tomatoes to the pan, toss in the oil/garlic/artichoke mixture and reduce heat to medium-low. Stir occasionally until tomatoes burst open, about 20-30 minutes. Add cayenne pepper, salt, and black pepper to taste and break tomatoes down further until they reach a saucy consistency.

Add all of the pesto ingredients to the **Tall Cup** and pulse with the **Extractor Blade** until ingredients form a thick paste. You may need to unscrew the blade and scrape the sides of the cup for an even consistency.

Top desired amount of barley with the tomato sauce, and spoon 1-2 Tbsp of pesto per serving on top. Enjoy!

Sweet Potato Hash and Salmon Scramble with Dill Pesto

Makes 2 servings of eggs, 2-4 servings of potatoes

This dish can be eaten for lunch or dinner, or for breakfast alongside a lighter veggie-filled NutriBlast. It's simple to make, and contains Omega-3 rich salmon, vitamin D-filled eggs, magnesium-rich chard, and blood-sugar stabilizing sweet potatoes—all of which have been linked to improved mood and reduced depression. If smoked salmon seems a bit too decadent for your budget, you can substitute half a can of wild-caught water-packed salmon.

Hash

- 1 Tbsp virgin cold-pressed coconut oil or extra-virgin olive oil
- 1 shallot, minced
- 1 ½ teaspoons smoked paprika
- 1 cup chopped Swiss chard
- 1 medium baked sweet potato*, cut into ½-inch cubes
- 1 Tbsp apple cider vinegar
- salt and pepper to taste

Heat oil in a heavy-bottomed skillet over medium heat.

Add all ingredients at once, stirring to coat evenly with oil.

Cook for 5-10 minutes to allow the bottom side to develop a crust, then flip to brown the other side, pressing down with a spatula to flatten the mixture, for another 5-10 minutes

To bake a sweet potato, preheat oven to 400 degrees. Prong the potato several times with a fork and bake on a parchment-lined sheet for 45 minutes.

Dill Pesto

- ¼ cup almonds
- 3 fresh chives
- 1 bunch fresh dill, roughly chopped
- Zest of 1 lemon
- ½ cup Extra Virgin olive oil
- ½ tsp salt
- pepper to taste

Add all ingredients to the **Tall Cup** and pulse until roughly puréed. Top each scramble serving with 1 – 2 tbs of pesto.

Scramble

- ½ Tbsp olive oil or cold-pressed virgin coconut oil
- 6 eggs—four egg whites and two whole eggs
- salt, to taste
- 1 scallion, thinly chopped
- 1 Tbsp fresh dill
- 4 ounces (about 4-5 slices) smoked salmon, cut into bite-sized pieces
- fresh ground pepper

Heat oil in a nonstick pan over low heat.

In a medium bowl, thoroughly whisk together the 4 egg whites, 2 whole eggs, scallion, salt, and pepper.

Add the eggs to the pan and let sit for one minute without stirring, until the bottom sets. Gently turn the runny eggs over until all of the pan's contents are firm (do not over-stir—you want the eggs to stay light and fluffy). Add the dill and smoked salmon and gently fold the eggs for another minute until ingredients are fully mixed and warmed. Enjoy!

Mood Improving
meals & treats

Packed Snack Chocolate Pudding
Serves 2

As a kid, there were few brown-bag lunch surprises better than a cup of chocolate Snack Pack pudding. Unpeeling the foil top, licking its underside, then digging in to the uniquely creamy, slightly wiggly chocolate-flavored goop was the crème de la crème (or gelatin) of cafeteria experiences.

Unfortunately, indulging in the artificially flavored, sweetened, and preserved "chocolate" treat spells more sorrow than joy at any age. Studies have linked processed food-laden diets to increased anxiety in both men and women.

But pudding lovers need not worry! This wholesome chocolate dessert tastes every bit as delicious as the old standard, but replaces high fructose corn syrup and gelatin with all-natural mood-boosting ingredients such as raw cacao, avocado, and banana. And while this version doesn't come in a sealed package, no one will judge you for pressing some tinfoil to the surface for personal licking purposes.

- 1 very ripe medium-sized banana, peeled and broken into chunks
- 1 ripe avocado, peeled and pit removed
- 4 Tbsp raw cacao powder
- 1 tsp vanilla extract
- ½ teaspoon almond extract
- ½ tsp cinnamon
- ½ cup almond milk
- Chopped toasted walnuts, cacao nibs, berries, etc for toppings (optional)

Add all ingredients to the **Tall Cup** and **extract** until smooth, about 40 seconds. The mixture should be the consistency of a brownie batter: thick, but still pourable. If the mixture seems too gloppy, add 1 to 2 more Tbsp of almond milk and **extract** once more.

Cover and refrigerate for 3-4 hours. Enjoy as is, or top with cacao nibs, walnuts, fresh berries, or any other complimentary whole food.

Date-me Truffles

Makes 12-16 servings

These tasty morsels are high in fiber and choc-full of happy nutrients like magnesium and omega-3 fatty acids. When enjoyed in moderation, these treats make an excellent mood-boosting dessert. They are, however, quite energy dense, so it's best to limit your indulgence to 1-2 truffles daily.

- 12 medjool dates, pits removed and soaked in water for 4-8 hours
- 1 cup toasted walnuts
- 3-4 Tbsp raw cacao powder
- 1 Tbsp cold-pressed coconut oil
- ¼ cup unsweetened shredded coconut, plus another ¼ cup for coating
- ½ tsp pure vanilla extract
- ½ tsp walnut extract
- ½ tsp cinnamon

Add all ingredients to the **Tall Cup** and pulse with the **Extractor Blade** until the dates form a thick paste with the walnuts and coconut evenly distributed throughout. You may need to unscrew the blade in between pulses and stir by hand to ensure an even mix.

Add reserved coconut to a small bowl. Form tablespoon-sized portions of the paste into balls and roll in shredded coconut to coat.

Arrange the truffles in layers between sheets of waxed paper in a food storage container, leaving a centimeter or two between each piece to avoid sticking. Cover and refrigerate for 2-3 hours before eating.

For more mood lifting recipes, please visit NutriLiving.com

Hormonal
issues *Help is just a blast away!*

Both men and women experience changes in sex hormone levels throughout their lives. An imbalance of these hormones can have negative effects on the body, ranging from mood swings to increased cancer risks.

Fortunately, a lot of the negative consequences of hormonal imbalance can be significantly reduced through nutrition. In women, including certain nutrients in the diet and eliminating other types of food from the diet can help to balance hormones, soothing the symptoms of PMS and/or menopause as a result. In men, proper nutrition can assist in boosting testosterone levels and prostate health.

The NutriBullet is the ideal tool for feeding the reproductive system the nutrients it needs to function properly. Drinking NutriBlasts full of nutrient-extracted plant foods ensures that your body absorbs all of the enzymes needed to set off the hormone manufacturing process. With healthy hormone functioning, your body, outlook, and life will be more balanced!

In addition to the NutriBlasts and recipes featured on the following pages, here's some more information on the link between balanced hormones and food:

The Age of UnSOYtainty
While soy is a bit of a controversial food, especially in regards to hormonal issues, studies show that a moderate intake (1-2x per week) of non-GMO, organic soy may help balance hormones.

Green Warriors
Dark green vegetables such as kale, collards, wheat and barley grass, seaweeds, and microalgae all inhibit the production of prostaglandin PGE2, a precursor to inflammation that can upset the female hormone balance.

Meat Your Maker

A diet high in animal protein, especially red meat, creates an acidic environment in the body, which leaches calcium from the bones. Studies link calcium loss with decreased hormone regulation in both men and women.

PLEASE CONSULT YOUR DOCTOR BEFORE CHANGING YOUR DIET, ESPECIALLY IF YOU ARE PREGNANT, NURSING, OR UNDERGOING TREATMENT/TAKING MEDICATION FOR HORMONAL IMBALANCE OR ANY OTHER MEDICAL CONDITION.

Hormonal issues
testimonials

" **Jennifer J.**

I finally purchased the NutriBullet after watching the infomercial for almost 6 months and it has been the best investment I have ever made. I am 44 years old and ever since I started my cycle at the ripe old age of 13, I have always had extremely painful periods with heavy bleeding. Over the past few years, my period has been so unbearable that I was considering having surgery because I thought that I had fibroids. My symptoms consisted of not only of heavy bleeding, but also of terrible cramping, nausea, headaches, lower back pain, and horrible mood swings. I felt like the exorcist the five days!

All of that changed when I received my NutriBullet. The first day of my cycle was normal with the usual pains and discomfort, but on the third day, I realized that my cycle was not very heavy at all. The real kicker was waking up at my usual 3 am ready to take a pain reliever, but I felt no cramping, no pain, nothing! I actually forgot that I was still on my period during the last two days because my mood was great! No headaches, no back pain, and no staying in the house. I felt great!

The next month, I had no cramping, back pain, or any of the painful symptoms I'd gotten used to over the past 30 years! I was actually able to go out and enjoy myself.

This month, I noticed that I was in serious pain the day my cycle was to start. The difference this month? I had gone a week without my NutriBullet drinks! But the good thing about the NutriBullet program is that once I felt that pain, I dragged myself to the store for my ingredients and made a batch to drink throughout the day. Within a day, I had no more cramping or back pain, and I was able to function as I had the previous months while drinking my NutriBullet green drinks religiously.

I was so excited about those results that I forgot to tell you that some of the other improvements I've seen! I have also lost 10 lbs and five inches in my stomach without exercising or even dieting. My joint pain from an old injury is also completely gone!

I hope this helps you as it continues to help me! "

" Lori W.

Hi. I'm a 53 years-young woman who began Menopause last year.
The NutriBullet has helped me eliminate my hot flashes by helping me get my daily requirement of vitamin E.

I discovered this by accident when I found that drinking one Blast per day kept the hot flashes at bay; if I went 7 days without a Blast, the hot flashes came back.

While Vitamin E may not help all women, it has worked for me. I am hoping to make it all the way through menopause without taking hormones and I know that the NutriBullet can help me make this hope a reality. "

Hormone Balancing
nutriblasts for her

Femme Fatale

The phrase 'femme fatale' can take on an entirely new meaning when describing a woman suffering from PMS! But not to worry – delicious B-vitamins, iron, and magnesium join forces in this Blast to give you the relief you need, letting you take on the world like the positive force you are!

- 1 cup spinach
- ¼ cup cooked garbanzo beans (Chickpeas)
- ½ cup strawberries
- 2 leaves mint
- ½ banana
- 1 tsp cinnamon
- Almond milk to **MAX LINE**

Add all ingredients to the **Tall Cup** and **extract** until smooth (about 30 seconds).

Girl's Best Friend

Ladies, sometimes our hormones get out of whack. Sometimes our bodies don't feel as good as we need. Sometimes outside stresses get the better of us and we just don't feel up to par. If that's the case, pal around with this NutriBlast. Its magnesium content boosts dopamine levels and helps your body process estrogen, Blasting those blahs and getting you pumped for your day!

- ½ **Tall Cup** Swiss Chard
- 1 banana
- 1 Tbsp Tahini (sesame seed paste)
- 6 almonds
- 6 cashews
- water to the **MAX LINE**

Add all ingredients to the **Tall Cup** and **extract** until smooth (about 30 seconds).

Nature's Candy

Got serious sweet cravings? Forget the sour sugared gummies and chocolate bars, and blend up the real thing with this delicious, fruit-filled Blast! Mild butter lettuce melds with juicy apples, pears, and blueberries for a decadent drink that's also loaded with antioxidants, fiber, and energizing minerals.

- 2 cups butter lettuce
- 1 pear
- 1 apple
- 1 cup blueberries
- 1 banana
- 1 Tbsp raw cacao powder
- water to the **MAX LINE**

Add all ingredients to the **Tall Cup** and **extract** until smooth (about 30 seconds).

Female Hormone Balancer

This nutrient-filled NutriBlast may help keep your body in check by assisting in the absorption of the nutrients it needs to balance out hormones.

- ½ **Tall Cup** butter lettuce
- ½ peach, pit removed
- ½ cup blueberries
- 3 brazil nuts
- 1 tsp maca powder
- water to **MAX LINE**

Add all ingredients to the **Tall Cup** and **extract** until smooth (about 30 seconds).

Hot Flash Cooler

Rich in antioxidants, vitamin K, and vitamin C, this special women's health concoction may help ease symptoms of menopause, including those dreaded hot flashes.

- ½ **Tall Cup** spinach
- ½ cup blueberries
- ½ cup tofu (organic)
- 1 Tbsp cacao (raw, powder, nibs, or beans)
- 1 tsp sesame seeds
- 10 cashews
- coconut milk beverage to **MAX LINE**

Add all ingredients to the **Tall Cup** and **extract** until smooth (about 30 seconds).

Hormone Balancing
meals & snacks for her

Anti-Bloat Bowl

Makes 6-12 Servings

This delicious brothy mix of vegetables contains diuretic properties to deflate a hormonally-bloated belly. The wide range of vegetables in this soup also play host to a smorgasbord of vitamins and minerals that help balance your system.

- 1 Tbsp cold pressed virgin coconut oil or extra virgin olive oil
- 1 onion, chopped
- 3 leeks, chopped
- 3 quarts (12 cups) filtered water
- 1/3 cup white miso OR 3 Tbsp low-sodium vegetable soup concentrate
- 1 Tbsp fennel seed
- 1 Tbsp caraway seed
- ½ Tbsp dried tarragon
- 5 carrots, chopped
- 6 celery stalks, chopped
- ½ head of green cabbage, thinly sliced or shredded
- 1 fennel bulb, thinly sliced
- 2 zucchinis, chopped into half-moon pieces
- ¼ cup cilantro or parsley, chopped

Heat oil in the base of an extra-large soup pot over medium heat. Add onion and chopped leeks and cook until browned and fragrant (about 4 minutes).

Reduce heat to low, and add water, miso, fennel seed, caraway seed, and tarragon. Stir until miso dissolves, then add carrots and celery and cook for 10 minutes. Add cabbage, fennel, and zucchini and cook for an additional 5-10 minutes, until all vegetables are tender, but not overcooked.

Enjoy right away or store in glass containers in the refrigerator for up to 5 days. The longer the soup sits, the more flavorful it will get. You can also divide the soup into batches and extract in the **Tall Cup** for a delicious puréed version.

Roasted Beet and Walnut Soup

Makes 2-3 Servings

Hormones have you feeling blue? A big bowl of this fuchsia soup might be all you need to lift that mood! Bright beets are loaded with B-vitamins—nutritional compounds lauded for their mood and energy-enhancing qualities. Pair them with Omega-3–rich walnuts, and you'll get a hefty dose of happy nutrients.

- 3 medium roasted beets*
- 1 Tbsp extra virgin olive oil, cold-pressed virgin coconut oil, or walnut oil
- ½ orange, peeled
- ½ medium onion, chopped
- 1 clove of garlic or ½ medium shallot, peeled
- 3 Tbsp raw walnuts
- 2 ½ cups organic vegetable broth
- sea salt to taste

Add all ingredients to the **Tall Cup** and **Extract** with the **Extractor Blade** until fully blended; about 45 seconds.

You can enjoy the soup chilled, or heat in a soup pot over medium heat for 5-10 minutes.

To roast beets, preheat oven to 375 degrees. Cut off beet greens (save for your morning NutriBlast— they're LOADED with nutrients) and the long tapered end of the root so your beets are roughly spherical. Scrub beets to remove any excess dirt, then dry them thoroughly. Wrap each beet individually in parchment paper, then wrap in foil so the packet holds its shape. Roast until tender—about 1-1.5 hours. Allow beets to cool before making the soup. You can roast the beets a day or two before preparing the soup to save time. They will keep in the refrigerator for up to 5 days.

Salmon Avocado Salad

Makes 2 servings

- 2 6-oz salmon filets
- 1 Tbsp olive oil, plus an additional Tbsp for salad dressing
- 2-4 cups bibb lettuce, torn into bite-sized pieces
- ½ ripe avocado, peeled and cubed
- ½ red onion, thinly sliced
- 10 cherry tomatoes, halved
- 1 Tbsp capers
- 2 Tbsp balsamic vinegar
- ½ Tbsp Dijon mustard

Preheat oven to 400 degrees. Arrange salmon on a parchment-lined baking sheet. Drizzle with olive oil, season with salt and pepper, and roast for 15-20 minutes until tender. Remove from oven and set aside

Add lettuce to two separate bowls. Divide avocado, onions, tomatoes, and capers over the two servings. Top each with 1 filet of salmon, skin removed.

Mix vinegar, mustard, and remaining Tbsp of olive oil in the **Tall Cup** with the **Extractor Blade** until emulsified. Pour dressing evenly over two salads. You can also multiply the recipe by four and save remaining salad dressing for later use. It will keep up to a month in the refrigerator.

Black Bean Dip

Enjoy this tasty dip with whole grain crackers or crispy raw veggies!

• 3 cups (or 2 cans organic, rinsed and drained) cooked black beans
• ½ onion, chopped
• 1/3 cup chopped cilantro
• 1 clove garlic, minced
• 1 small de-seeded jalapeno pepper, diced
• 4 cherry tomatoes, rinsed
• ¼ red bell pepper, chopped
• juice from 1 lime
• ¼ tsp ground cumin
• ¼ tsp chili powder
• salt and pepper to taste

Add all ingredients to the **Tall Cup** and **Extract** with the **Extractor Blade**, pulsing and pausing to scrape the sides of the cup until ingredients form a thick paste.

Store in the refrigerator for up to 5 days.

Choco-Banana Bacchanal

Sometimes things are clichés because they're true. Whether premenstrual, menopausal, pregnant, or suffering any other hormonal issue, every girl at some point has to have chocolate. This recipe makes a frosty, delicious, über-chocolatey treat using the natural sweetness of frozen bananas and the deep cocoa bite of raw cacao. If you're feeling really wild, rage with your hormones and top a bowl of this frosty delight with some toasted almonds or walnuts. Who knew being hormonal could be such a NutriBlast!

- 2 bananas, frozen in chunks
- 2-3 Tbsp raw cacao
- 2-4 Tbsp unsweetened vanilla almond milk
- 1 Tbsp chopped toasted almonds or walnuts (optional)

Allow frozen bananas to thaw for 2-3 minutes

Add bananas, cacao, and almond milk to the **Tall Cup** and pulse with the **Extractor Blade** until the mixture is fully blended. You may need to shake the cup in between pulses to ensure even blending.

Pour into a bowl, top with nuts, and enjoy!

Hormone Balancing
nutriblasts for him

Dude Defender

This dude-defending Blast contains lots of lycopene - an antioxidant known to protect against prostate cancer. Add pumpkin or sunflower seeds for an extra boost of zinc, which is great for boosting immunity and testosterone levels (not to mention libido).

- ½ **Tall Cup** spinach
- 1 cup(s) watermelon
- ½ grapefruit
- 2 Tbsp pumpkin or sunflower seeds
- water to the **MAX LINE**

Add all ingredients to the **Tall Cup** and **extract** until smooth (about 30 seconds).

Male Hormone Balancer

Though hormonal imbalance tends to be viewed as a female concern, men also suffer from hormone-related issues. Whip this one up when you're feeling less than your normal wood-chopping, cattle roping, mammoth-hunting self.

- ¼ small beets
- 10 grapes
- 2 floret(s) broccoli
- 15 blueberries
- ¼ cup(s) pumpkin seeds
- 1 Tbsp olive oil
- water to the **MAX LINE**

Add all ingredients to the **Tall Cup** and **extract** until smooth (about 45 seconds).

N'Zinc

Feeling a little tired? Sluggish? Out of touch with the young buck you once were? You may be suffering from low testosterone. Testosterone levels naturally decrease as we age, but simple dietary changes can help normalize the body's testosterone production—increasing energy levels and lifting a lethargic libido. The mineral zinc, specifically, has been shown to regulate testosterone levels in men of all ages. This NutriBlast incorporates several plant-based sources of the mineral.

- ½ **Tall Cup** kale
- 1 banana
- 1 Tbsp pumpkin seeds
- 1 Tbsp sesame seeds
- ½ cup steel-cut oats, cooked
- water or unsweetened almond milk to the **MAX LINE**

Add all ingredients to the **Tall Cup** and **extract** until smooth (about 45 seconds).

Hormone Balancing
meals & snacks for him

Tomato-Mushroom Tartine

Makes 2 servings

You might not think there's anything manly about the word *tartine*, but this open-faced sandwich contains zinc-filled mushrooms and eggs, plus lycopene-rich stewed tomatoes, giving you double dose of testosterone-boosting and prostate cancer-fighting minerals. Get over your prejudices and eat this tartine like a man.

- 1-2 Tbsp olive oil or cold-pressed virgin coconut oil
- ½ onion, thinly sliced
- 2 cloves of garlic, minced
- 1 cup shiitake mushrooms, washed, dried, and sliced
- 8 organic canned plum tomatoes, roughly chopped
- ½ teaspoon fresh thyme
- ¼ tsp salt
- pepper to taste
- 2 organic eggs
- Two 1-inch slices of crusty, fresh-baked whole grain bread, toasted*

Heat oil in a medium saucepan over medium heat. Add the onions and sauté until translucent, then add garlic and mushrooms and cook for another 5 minutes until mushrooms soften and onions and garlic are soft and golden brown (you may need to add

more oil at this point, as mushrooms tend to soak up a lot).

Stir in the tomatoes, thyme and salt and pepper. Increase heat to high and cook until the tomatoes break down into a saucy consistency, about 5 minutes. Reduce heat to low and make two divots in the vegetable mixture. Crack eggs into the divots, cover pan, and cook for 5-10 minutes, flipping halfway through until eggs reach desired consistency. 5 minutes yields a runny yolk, while 10 minutes will cook the yolk all the way through.

Spoon half of the tomato-mushroom mixture over half of toasted bread and top with egg. Dig in.

To toast bread in oven, place on a parchment-lined baking sheet and bake at 350 degrees for 10 minutes, flipping halfway through to ensure even crispness. Bread should be crisp on the outside and soft and chewy inside.

Tilapia Tacos with Fresh Slaw and Mango Salsa

This delicious, refreshing meal is loaded with male endocrine enhancers! The tacos' tilapia contains testosterone-boosting B-vitamins, while the slaw's cabbage content promotes beneficial estrogen metabolism and helps restore a healthy hormonal balance in the body. This slaw also contains zinc-filled pumpkin and sesame seeds.

NOTE: The tilapia cooks quickly. To avoid overcooking (and general mealtime chaos), we suggest preparing your slaw before you broil the fish. Multitask by chopping slaw ingredients while the broiler preheats, or make the side dish a day or two ahead of time—it will keep in the refrigerator for up to five days.

Fresh Slaw

Serves 6

- 1 head of purple cabbage, shredded
- 1 small yellow pepper
- 1 green apple, cored and sliced into matchsticks
- 1 ripe avocado, diced
- 2 scallions, thinly sliced
- Juice of 2 limes
- 1/4 cup toasted pumpkin seeds
- 2 Tbsp black sesame seeds
- ¼ cup chopped cilantro or parsley
- 1/4 teaspoon sea salt
- Fresh ground black pepper, to taste

Add all ingredients to a large salad bowl, squeeze lime juice on top, and toss until ingredients are fully mixed.

Mango Salsa

- Flesh of 1 ripe mango, peeled and pitted
- ½ cucumber
- 1 jalapeno pepper, halved with seeds removed
- ¼ avocado
- ¼ cup fresh lime juice
- ½ tsp dried cumin
- 5 sprigs fresh cilantro, stems trimmed

Add all ingredients to the **Tall Cup** and pulse with the **Extractor Blade** until puréed. Pour 2 tablespoons over each taco.

Tilapia Tacos

Serves 2 (2 Tacos per serving)

- ½ tablespoon olive oil
- Two six-ounce tilapia filets
- ½ tsp ground coriander
- ½ tsp ground cumin
- salt and fresh ground pepper to taste
- 4 organic, non-GMO corn tortillas
- Garnishes (all optional): Thinly sliced radishes, organic salsa, fresh guacamole, avocado slices, chopped tomato, cilantro sprigs
- 2 limes, cut into wedges

Preheat oven broiler to low (allow to heat for at least 20 minutes).

Rinse tilapia filets and pat dry. Place on a foil-lined baking sheet or broiler pan. Drizzle with olive oil and season with coriander, cumin, salt, and pepper. Broil on low roughly 8 inches from the heat source for 6-8 minutes, until fish is cooked through but tender.

Prepare garnishes as the fish cooks. Wrap tortillas in a damp cloth towel and microwave for 30 seconds.

Break fish Into pleces and divide among the four tortillas. Garnish as desired and squeeze lime over the tacos.

Serve alongside Fresh Slaw.

Spiced Seeds

Makes 8 Servings

Get your snack on with this satisfying mix of zinc-filled seeds. While you don't want to go crazy with sweeteners, the boron found in honey has been linked to heightened testosterone.

- 1 cup raw sunflower seeds
- 1 cup raw pumpkin seeds
- 1 ½ Tbsp cold-pressed virgin coconut oil
- 1 Tbsp raw honey
- 1 tsp sea salt
- ¼ tsp cayenne pepper
- 1 tsp ground cumin
- ½ tsp cinnamon

Preheat the oven to 350 degrees.

Add all ingredients to a large bowl and knead with fingers until the seeds are evenly coated with the oil/honey/spice mixture.

Spread mixture evenly on a lightly greased parchment-lined baking sheet and bake for 7 minutes. Flip with a spatula and bake for another 5 minutes until seeds are crisp and golden-brown.

Fruitful Salad

Serves 2

The fruits in this medley contain nutrients linked to increased libido and heartier sperm. Enough said.

- 1 cup of grapes
- 6 Figs, quartered
- ½ cup pomegranate Seeds
- ½ Tbsp raw honey
- 1 Tbsp fresh lemon or lime juice

Combine fruit in a medium bowl.

Combine honey and lemon juice in the **Tall Cup** and **extract** until fully mixed. Pour over fruit and enjoy!

More than
you can chew

Blasting to improve digestive issues

You can't get any more direct than the link between food and digestion. The whole point of the digestive system is to break food down into a state where it can be absorbed into the body and converted to energy. In general, when we feed our body well, our digestion functions well.

There are, however, many issues that can emerge during the digestive process. Sometimes, even the healthiest food can upset a sensitive digestive system. This is where the NutriBullet comes in handy. Our little machine breaks fibrous, nutrient-dense fruits and vegetables down into liquid form—essentially pre-digesting them for you—so your digestive system does not have to strain to break these foods down itself.

Whether you suffer from the occasional bout of indigestion, constipation, or diarrhea, or have been diagnosed with a chronic condition like GERD, IBS, or Crohn's disease, the NutriBullet can be an incredibly helpful addition to your lifestyle!

Before you start Blasting, here is a bit of information for you to chew on:

Cider Fighter
Apple cider vinegar can be used to help decrease symptoms of acid reflux and calm an upset stomach. Add 1 tsp to a cup of ginger tea for a powerful digestive soothing tonic.

Flora Plan
There are about 500 different species of bacteria living in your digestive tract. The average healthy adult carries 5 to 8 pounds of "flora" inside them at all times. The total number of bacteria (both "good" and "bad") in your gut exceeds the number of cells your body contains 10 fold.

Foods such as kimchi, kombucha, sauerkraut, miso, and kefirs are great sources of "healthy bacteria" also known as probiotics. It's important to keep those bacteria thriving by feeding them prebiotic foods such as bananas, garlic, oats, asparagus, jicama, and almonds. A healthy gut flora will support proper digestion and may help heal a myriad of the body's ailments.

Intestinal Intelligence

Your small intestine literally has a mind of its own. That "gut instinct" is actually part of the enteric nervous system (ENS). Aside from your brain, your gut is the only system in your body that has a nervous system dedicated entirely to itself. This is why some foods affect your mood and why mental stress may hinder proper digestion.

PLEASE CONSULT YOUR DOCTOR BEFORE MAKING ANY DRASTIC CHANGES TO YOUR DIET, ESPECIALLY IF YOU ARE PREGNANT, NURSING, OR UNDERGOING TREATMENT/TAKING MEDICATION FOR DIGESTIVE ISSUES OR ANY OTHER MEDICAL CONDITION.

Digestive issues
testimonials

" June K.

http://nutribulletblog.com/share-your-story/#comment-9042

Thank you so much for the NutriBullet; it has changed my life!

My husband and I are over the road truck drivers. We drive team and are gone from home for up to 6 weeks at a time. This past summer I stayed home while he ran equipment for a concert tour. My goal was to finally find a way to eat healthy and lose some weight, something we could both do easily on the road.

I have also suffered with severe IBS since childhood and was taking up to 7 Immodium a day to help with my symptoms. I had tried all the probiotic meds available without any relief. As you can imagine, having IBS on a 18-wheeler is really difficult. We could be in the middle of nowhere for hundreds of miles. It affected my ability to drive and I would go without eating because of the lack of facilities. I was planning on telling my husband when he returned that I could no longer drive with him because of my IBS.

Well, what can I say? We have both lost a noticeable amount of weight and my IBS is completely GONE. I can't begin to tell you what a relief it is and what freedom it has given back to me. I missed out on so many family functions because of my symptoms. I told my husband my life consisted of stress worrying about my symptoms. I was constantly dehydrated from the many trips to the bathroom and I couldn't lose weight because of my irregular eating schedule.

My friends and family have noticed how the NutriBullet has changed my life, and 7 of them have bought their own! I just ordered two more to give my daughters for Christmas and I need to buy one more for the truck!

Thanks so much for giving me back my freedom to keep working out here delivering America's goods! "

Barb P.

I have always had problems with my digestive system. I have IBS and have had two thoracic surgeries for GERD as well as a colostomy for diverticulosis. I knew had to adjust my life and eating habits.

I purchased a NutriBullet and began to experiment. I had not been able to eat citrus fruit or juice for years because it exacerbated my GERD. When I incorporated citrus into my NutriBullet recipes along with vegetables and other fiber-filled foods, not only could I tolerate it, but I have been able to stop all medications! I finally do not feel bloated or have the burning reflux I had.

I am so grateful for this product. Along with exercise and heallthy meal planning, it has changed my life and eliminated my need for medication!!!

Janine F.

The NutriBullet has made such a huge difference in my life after only using it for two weeks!

I have Crohn's disease and have not been able to eat fruits, nuts and vegetables the "normal" way for more than 20 years.

When I am having a stricture – inflammation of the inside walls of the intestines – I normally go down to liquids and very, very soft foods. I have had surgery that removed part of my intestines, so I am unable to digest many foods and multivitamins. My nutrition, needless to say, has been terrible... until I found the NutriBullet.

On a painful day when I cannot eat solids, I normally would only be able to eat chicken broth with some scrambled eggs swirled in, some types of juice, and water. Most fruits and vegetables, especially raw ones, were very painful to digest. Now I can make NutriBlasts from vegetables and fruits that I haven't eaten in almost 20 years!

I can't tell you how this machine has changed my life. I have been making anti-inflammatory Blasts in the NutriBullet, and have really been feeling much better than I was. I am truly grateful to have found it!

I am feeling so much better physically and I'm relieved to know that I am now getting nutrition I was unable to get for years. I encourage others who suffer from Crohn's disease to try this fabulous machine. Thank you so much for helping me get nutrition I was unable to get for so many years, and improving the way I feel!

Jay C.

I'm a walking advertisement.

I was diagnosed with Ulcerative Colitis several years ago. Actually, the doctor was fearful that the Colitis was in fact Crohn's disease. However, in last week's exam, the doctor proclaimed the disease was in remission, as all appeared normal with no sign of Crohn's.

With the NutriBullet, my meal combinations are so easy that they are becoming a regular part of my day-to-day life. I've lost about 10 pounds in the past 6 weeks. On most days, I have had a NutriBlast both in the morning for breakfast and in the evenings prior to working out. I'll have one or two regular, but smaller, meals daily and the rest are the 2 healthy Blasts consisting of greens (kale/spinach/broccoli), berries (blueberries/goji berries/strawberries), nuts (walnuts or almonds), supplements (hemp/cacao/maca/flax/chia), and other various veggies/fruits.

I just add water and, with the help of my NutriBullet, I've been feeling rather outstanding. Even the arthritis pains in my hands and feet are gone!

I'm amazed at how easy it is; adjusting your diet (and health) is really just a state of mind.

Digestive
nutriblasts

Monique B.'s
Stomach Soother

This reader recipe contains ginger to calm a nauseous or unsettled stomach, as well as lemon, carrot, cucumber, and celery to flush out toxins and reduce bloating!

- ½ **Tall Cup** of spinach
- ¼ of an organic cucumber
- ½ celery stalk
- 1 carrot
- ½" piece of ginger
- ¼ of a whole lemon (peeled
- water to the **MAX LINE**

Add all ingredients to the **Tall Cup** and **extract** until smooth (about 45 seconds).

FunnFrugalLady's Digestive Delight

Another user-submitted recipe, this NutriBlast contains a wide variety of natural digestive aids. High-fiber chia seeds form a gel-like consistency when combined with water, adding bulk for satiety and promoting bowel regularity. Pectin-filled apples and high-fiber flax have similar digestive effects. Peppermint contains methanol, a natural nausea-soothing compound, while papayas contain papain and chymopapain, two powerful enzymes that help break down proteins in the digestive tract.

- 1 handful raw collards
- 1/3 cup papaya
- 1/2 apple
- 1/2 orange
- 1/2 teaspoon cinnamon
- ¼ lemon, peel removed
- 2 fresh peppermint leaves
- 1/2 teaspoon chia seeds
- ½ tsp flax seed
- Water to the **MAX LINE**

Add all ingredients to the **Tall Cup** and **extract** until smooth (about 45 seconds).

Lisa's Mover and Shaker

NutriLiving user Lisa C.R. submitted a version of this elixir for digestive efficiency. Parsley, cucumber, and celery serve as natural diuretics that eliminate unnecessary water and toxins from your system. Apple cider vinegar works to stimulate the stomach's production of hydrochloric acid (HCL), helping it break foods down more efficiently, and detoxify the digestive tract with enzymes that help eliminate unwanted yeast and bacteria. Finally, ginger's anti-nausea properties can reduces the physical discomfort that sometimes accompanies digestive issues.

- ½ **Tall Cup** kale
- 4 sprigs fresh parsley
- ½ cucumber, washed or rind removed
- 2 stalks celery, chopped
- ½ pear
- 1 ½-inch piece of ginger root, peel removed
- 1 Tbsp Bragg's Apple Cider Vinegar
- water to the **MAX LINE**

Add all ingredients to the **Tall Cup** and **extract** until smooth (about 45 seconds).

Digestive
meals

Roasted Veggie Bisque
Serves 2-3

Eating for proper digestion can seem like a catch-22: while intestines need fiber to function properly, too much roughage can trigger digestive distress! This delicious soup solves the problem, giving you the fiber you need in an easily digestible puréed form. Its creamy texture also gives you decadence sans-high fat dairy, a food group known to irritate sensitive systems.

- 1 cup of cauliflower, broken into evenly sized florets
- 1 cup of broccoli, broken into evenly sized florets
- 1 cup baby carrots
- 1 yellow squash, cut into half-moons
- ½ onion
- 1 Tbsp olive oil
- 1 tsp salt
- 3 cups vegetable broth
- ½ cup cooked old-fashioned oats
- 1 Tbsp dried dill
- pinch of cayenne pepper
- 1 Tbsp lemon juice
- salt and pepper to taste

Preheat oven to 400 degrees.

Add vegetables to a large bowl and coat with olive oil and salt. Arrange evenly on a parchment-lined baking pan. Roast for 20-30 minutes until soft and caramelized. Allow to cool completely to room temperature for 1 hour, or refrigerate for 30 minutes.

Extract the soup in two batches:

Add ½ of the vegetables, 1 ½ cups veggie broth, and ¼ cup cooked oats to the **Tall Cup**. **Extract** with the **Extractor Blade** until smooth—about 1 minute—and transfer to a medium-sized pot.

Repeat the same process for the second batch, but add dill into the mixture. Add to the pot, turn the burner to medium, and stir in cayenne pepper, lemon juice, and salt and pepper to taste. Heat to desired temperature and serve.

Avocado Alfredo

Serves 2

This dish replaces the heavy cream and simple carbohydrate ingredients of traditional fettuccini Alfredo with a nourishing avocado sauce and quinoa pasta, making it a delicious treat for those with dairy or gluten intolerance.

- 1 8-oz package of gluten-free quinoa spaghetti
- 1 ripe avocado
- juice of ½ lemon
- 1 clove garlic
- ½ tsp kosher salt
- 2 Tbsp olive oil
- ¼ cup basil
- ½ bunch fresh parsley, finely chopped (to garnish)
- cracked black pepper

Cook pasta according to package instructions.

Extract avocado, lemon juice, garlic, salt, and olive oil in the **Tall Cup** until smooth. Unscrew the blade, add basil, and **extract** once more until fully mixed. Divide the sauce over two bowls of hot pasta and garnish with parsley and black pepper.

Note: any extra servings of the pasta/sauce mixture should be enjoyed cold, as avocado does not re-heat well.

Digestive
snacks & treats

Sweet Potato Oven Fries with Yogurt Aioli

Makes 2 servings of fries, plus extra aioli

Easy on the digestive system like regular potatoes but nutritionally denser, sweet potatoes make a great side dish for anyone suffering from a sensitive system. If your system can handle dairy, dip your sweet tots in our probiotic-filled yogurt aioli for added flavor and digestive benefits. If you'd prefer a dairy-free dip, feel free to replace the yogurt in this recipe with Greek-style cultured coconut milk.

- 2 medium sweet potatoes, washed and dried
- ½ Tbsp olive oil, plus another ½ Tbsp for the aioli
- ¼ tsp chili powder
- ½ tsp kosher salt
- Fresh cracked pepper to taste
- ½ cup 2% plain Greek yogurt or plain Greek-style cultured coconut milk
- ½ Tbsp honey, brown rice syrup OR ¼ tsp maple syrup
- ½ bunch fresh cilantro (stems mostly removed)
- Juice from ¼ to ½ lemon, to taste
- salt and cracked black pepper, to taste

Preheat oven to 400 degrees. Cut sweet potatoes in half lengthwise, then into long strips.
Add the potato wedges to a large bowl and coat with oil, chili powder, salt, and pepper.
Arrange potatoes on a parchment-lined baking sheet and bake for 20-30 minutes, turning halfway through until crisped on the outside, but soft in the middle.

While the potatoes bake, add yogurt, ½ Tbsp olive oil, sweetener, cilantro, and lemon juice to the **Tall Cup** and **extract** until cilantro is finely chopped.

Allow fries to cool for 10 minutes before eating.
Aioli will keep in the refrigerator for up to 5 days.

Orange Delight Blast

Papaya and pineapple pair with ginger in this sweet, tropical-tasting blast. The enzymes papain in papaya and bromelain in pineapple are both known to help the body digest and absorb protein. Add some plain Greek yogurt or Greek-style cultured coconut milk to this treat for a probiotic boost!

- ¾ cup frozen papaya
- ½ cup frozen pineapple
- One ½-inch piece of ginger, peeled
- ½ cup nonfat plain Greek yogurt or plain Greek-style cultured coconut milk
- ½ Tbsp raw honey, agave, or brown rice syrup
- Juice of 1 lime
- ¾ cup unsweetened almond milk
- ½ cup ice

Add all ingredients to the **Tall Cup** and **extract** until smooth, about 45 seconds.

Athletic
extraction

Blasting to achieve peak athletic performance
and fast recovery.

This section focuses on using NutriBlasts to prepare and recover from various athletic pursuits. The NutriBullet is an ideal tool for athletes, as it both hydrates and delivers exceptional nutrients to the system, feeding muscles with the elements they need to heal and strengthen faster.

Additionally, fueling your body with liquids instead of food helps you avoid cramps before a workout, and delivers much-needed nutrients to the body post-workout when the appetite tends to be suppressed.

PLEASE CONSULT YOUR DOCTOR BEFORE MAKING ANY DRASTIC CHANGES TO YOUR DIET, ESPECIALLY IF YOU ARE PREGNANT, NURSING, OR UNDERGOING TREATMENT/TAKING MEDICATION FOR DIGESTIVE ISSUES OR ANY OTHER MEDICAL CONDITION.

Athletic Extraction
testimonials

" ## Michael P.

For years, I led a sedentary, unhealthy lifestyle and in 2008, I weighed 300 pounds and had cancer. During my cancer treatment, I was unable to swallow and was fed through a feeding tube. I was tired, beat up and I realized this was no way to live life. After my chemotherapy and radiation was complete and my cancer was in remission, I decided to make changes in my life.

The first change I made was in my diet and exercise, which was a pretty simple plan. My first walk was about 200 yards, but I was determined and made it a goal each day to go one telephone pole farther, which I did. I also decided that, when I was well enough to eat again, I would do my best to change my diet. This was the hard part.

The whole thing was a slow process; I guess it was really an evolution, an ever-changing learning process. Fast forward 5 years to 2013, all the changes have been made and I have run 7 marathons and I've lived a pretty healthy lifestyle. I was supposed to run the 2013 LA Marathon, but during training, I was injured and required surgery. I was unable to exercise like I wanted; I was eating everything in sight and I had put on an extra 10 pounds. Even though I wasn't running the marathon, I decided to go to the LA Marathon Expo.

NutriBullet was at the Expo demonstrating and selling the NutriBullet. My friend, whom I was with, had one, bought one for me and told me to just try it. I took the NutriBullet home, read the information book that it came with, watched the infomercial on TV and tried it. I was amazed at how good everything was and how good I felt after having a Blast. A month later, I'm down 15 pounds, I'm exercising again and I look forward to each Blast.

The NutriBullet is not a diet, it is not a fad; it is a choice you make each day to live a better life. By making small changes a little at a time, soon those small changes add up. You lose weight, you have more energy, you look better and you feel better. There is nothing more encouraging than getting up in the morning and stepping on the scale and seeing the results. I love the NutriBullet! "

Mike W.

I started drinking NutriBlasts about a year ago, I was looking to improve how I felt and to improve my performance when working out. Boy, have I hit a homerun!! I feel hundreds times better and have seen my performance soar, more so on my running. I have gotten into the Paleo diet and this helps a lot. My go to is spinach, kale, banana, avocado, a little peanut butter and any in-season fruit, yum!

Pre-workout
nutriblasts

Beet the Competition

This pretty Blast is a favorite of Team NutriBullet—our team of runners who competed in the L.A. Marathon!

- 1 cup of spinach
- 1 scoop of NutriBullet Superfood Superboost
- 1/2 cup blueberries
- 3-4 strawberries
- 1 banana
- 1/4 of a beet (raw or steamed and completely cooled to room temperature)
- Fill **Tall Cup** up to **MAX LINE** with coconut water

Extract with the **Extractor Blade** until smooth—about 35 seconds with a cooled steamed beat, or 50 seconds with a raw beet.

Smooth Moves

- 1.5 cups water
- 1 cup pineapple chunks (frozen)
- 1/2 small ripe avocado, peeled and pitted
- 2 cups spinach

Extract with the **Extractor Blade** until smooth—about 45 seconds.

Almonds Reign Supreme

Fueling for endurance requires a readily available and long-lasting source of energy. This NutriBlast provides simple sugars from bananas and dates that are slowly released into the blood stream when combined with the protein and healthy fats found in almond butter.

- Handful of spinach
- 1 -2 Tbsp almond butter
- 2 dates (pits removed)
- 1 banana (peeled)
- Almond milk to the **MAX LINE** and **extract**

Blue's Go-To

Would you like to perform like professional marathon runner and Team NutriBullet captain Blue Benadum? Drink his personal favorite 30 minutes to 1 hour before your run. If running within an hour of eating causes GI distress, be sure to Blast earlier to allow proper digestion. Rolled oats thicken the mixture, while the maca found in the Superfood Powerboost will increase stamina and energy for the tough road ahead.

- Handful of kale
- 1 carrot
- ¼ cup uncooked rolled oats (you may cook if desired)
- ½ cup berries of choice
- 1 Tbsp chia seeds (or a scoop of NutriBullet Superfood Superboost)
- Handful of ice
- Almond milk to the **MAX LINE**

Extract with the **Extractor Blade** until smooth (about 45 seconds).

Post-workout
nutriblasts

Jennipher W.'s Cool Down Cooler

- Half **Tall Cup** up of mixed greens
- 1 frozen banana
- 1 scoop of vegan vanilla protein powder
- water or coconut water to **MAX LINE**

Extract with the **Extractor Blade** until smooth (about 35 seconds).

Pumpkin Up

- 1/2 cup pumpkin puree
- 1 cup ice
- 4 oz low fat organic cottage cheese OR organic silken tofu
- 1 tsp pumpkin pie spice
- 1 cup unsweetened almond milk

Extract with the **Extractor Blade** until smooth (about 45 seconds).

Whirled Peas

- 1/3 medium banana
- 2 Tbsp hemp seed
- 1/2 cup frozen mixed berries
- 1/4 cup walnuts
- 1/2 cup frozen green peas
- 1 cup coconut milk beverage (NOT the high-calorie canned kind)

Extract with the **Extractor Blade** until smooth (about 45 seconds).

Bean Scene

- 6 large strawberries
- 1/2 cup chickpeas/garbanzo beans, well rinsed or home cooked
- 1 cup of unsweetened almond milk
- 6 drops vanilla extract
- 6 drops coconut extract
- 1 drop liquid stevia

Extract with the **Extractor Blade** until smooth (about 30 seconds).

Blue's Go-To When Thru

Kick Blue's go-to pre-workout NutriBlast up a notch for a post workout treat! Take the pre-workout recipe with the same name and add ½ cup cooked quinoa. Feel free to change the almond milk to coconut water if desired. Coconut water is a great source of potassium, an important electrolyte that gets lost in sweat. Electrolytes are minerals that affect your body's fluid balance, acidity of the blood, muscle function, and other important processes.

- Handful of kale
- 1 carrot
- ¼ cup uncooked rolled oats (you may cook if desired)
- ½ cup berries of choice
- 1 Tbsp chia seeds (or a scoop of Superfood Powerboost)
- Handful of ice
- ½ cup cooked quinoa
- coconut water to the **MAX LINE**

Extract with the **Extractor Blade** until smooth (about 45 seconds).

Bonus
snack

Chocolate Energy Balls

- Enjoy these little bites of fuel for a quick and easy source of pre or post-workout nutrients!
- 1/2 cup almond flour
- ¾ cup medjool dates, pits removed
- pinch of himalayan sea salt
- 1/4 cup packed mint leaves
- 1/4 cup unsweetened cocoa powder
- 1-2 Tbsp coconut or almond milk

Add all ingredients to the **Tall Cup** and pulse with the **Extractor Blade** until ingredients form a sticky paste.

Roll the mixture into balls and refrigerate for 3-4 hours before enjoying!

NOTES
